CONCEPTS OF ELECTRICITY

Student Workbook

Written by: **Lawrence P. Larsen**
Senior Educational Media Designer

EB-3100-40
HEATH COMPANY
BENTON HARBOR, MICHIGAN 49022
595-3943-01

ISBN 0-87119-163-6

CONTENTS

INTRODUCTION

Your Student Workbook contains fourteen exercises and six unit examinations. The exercises reinforce the concepts presented in your textbook. The unit examinations verify that you have attained the objectives established for each unit.

Before you begin the exercises, **read** the following introductory material. There, you will find a description of the equipment you will be using, along with several tips and cautions concerning that equipment. Following the equipment section is a review of hand tools and general safety tips. Next, the exercise format is described. This is followed by an exercise "schedule," that shows you when to perform a specific exercise. Finally, all of the parts that are used in the exercises are listed and identified.

The back of this text contains a set of "Exercise Answer Sheets." These are perforated "tear-out" pages that can be used by your instructor to verify the results you attain in each exercise. The answer blanks and tables within these sheets match the answer blanks and tables within the exercises.

Equipment

You will need several pieces of equipment if you are to complete the exercises. This equipment includes a trainer where you build and power the exercises; one or more meters to measure AC and DC current, AC and DC voltage, and resistance; an oscilloscope; and several hand tools and a soldering iron.

TRAINER

The exercises are designed to work on any of three Heath Trainers. These include the ET-3100(A/B), the ET-3600, and the ET-1000. You can also use a simple breadboard, two potentiometers, and individual power supplies in place of the trainer. The following minimum capabilities are required for the individual equipment:

1. A power supply capable of producing 0 to ±15 volts DC at 200 milliamps.
2. A power supply capable of producing 15 volts AC (60 Hertz) at 200 milliamps.
3. An audio signal generator capable of producing both sine waves and square waves at frequencies from 200 Hz to 20 kHz.
4. A 0 to 1000 ohm potentiometer.
5. A 0 to 100 kilohm potentiometer.

TEST EQUIPMENT

In addition to the trainer, you will need a volt-ohm-milliammeter and an oscilloscope. Although you can use a multi-function digital meter, there are a couple of places in the exercises where the voltage and current levels can give you an erroneous reading. Therefore, we recommend that you have access to an analog meter for those measurements if you wish to use a digital meter for most of your measurements. While a multi-function meter is most convenient, you can also use individual meters to measure voltage, resistance, and current.

Any type of single- or dual-trace oscilloscope will work for the following exercises. You will use the scope to observe relatively low frequency sine and square wave signals, and the output from several generator circuits.

GENERAL TIPS AND CAUTIONS

The following information will help you improve the accuracy of your exercises by showing you little "tricks-of-the-trade."

1. Be sure that all powered equipment is connected to the same power source. This will establish a common ground reference and prevent ground loops. By definition, a ground loop is an electrical path between two separate grounds. If these grounds are at different potentials, they create an unwanted current path that can cause instability or measurement errors.

2. Make sure you **DO NOT** inadvertently insert a ground into the circuit under test. This could occur, for example, if your test equipment reference (ground) lead is earth ground.

   Use an ohmmeter set to $R \times 1$ to see if the test equipment reference lead is earth grounded. Measure between the reference lead and the center prong on the Trainer's power plug. If the reading is zero, your equipment is earth grounded. If it is earth grounded, all measurements MUST be referenced to ground.

3. Remember that the voltage and function generator frequency controls on the Trainer represent approximate values. If you want or need greater accuracy, monitor the voltage with a voltmeter and monitor the frequency with a frequency counter or oscilloscope.

4. The accuracy of your exercises may vary slightly with those of other students or examples given in the text. This is because of component part tolerances, meter calibration, and the individual interpolation of the meter's reading.

Hand Tools And Safety

A basic hand tool can be any hand-held object that aids you in performing a task. It can be a labor saving device if it is used properly, or an accident looking for a place to happen if it is used improperly. That leads us to an interesting statistic: The single biggest cause of accidents is the failure to think. Now I'm sure you would agree that events and projects should not be "happenings." Rather, they should always be developed from, or accomplished with, the aid of a plan. That means, you have to do a little thinking. However, it's easy to become complacent (bored) or think you know it all, when it comes to using hand tools. When that happens, you become an accident waiting to happen. How many times have you heard, or said, "I have done this job so many times I could do it in my sleep." That statement represents a dangerous attitude, one that could someday cause you a serious injury. Safety is an attitude, and acting in an unsafe manner is foolish.

This section will describe several of the tools that you will use in these exercises and in possible future projects. It will also cover areas of hand tool and electrical safety. Keep in mind, however, that while we can tell you what to do and what not to do, we can't do your thinking for you.

HAND TOOL SAFETY

Safety is more a state of mind than an exact science. Generally speaking, If you think safe, you'll be safe. Here are a few common sense guidelines that should be followed when using hand tools:

1. Keep the work area clean and free of unneeded objects.
2. Don't hurry an operation.
3. Don't work when you are tired.
4. Check the condition of your tools before you use them.
5. Use the correct tool for the job.
6. Develop and follow a job (project) plan.
7. Wear protective clothing and safety equipment.
8. Don't take short cuts.
9. Don't leave power tools unattended.
10. Don't take anything for granted, double check every detail.
11. Remember the job isn't finished until you clean and store your tools, and the work area is cleaned.

ELECTRONIC HAND TOOLS

Most common hand tools (hammer, wrench, pliers, etc.) are too large to be of much use in electronic work, although you may use them to get at the circuit or component needing repair. Figure 1 illustrates many of the specialized tools used for electronic equipment repair. For the following exercises, you will use the long nose pliers, diagonal cutters, wire strippers, and a soldering iron.

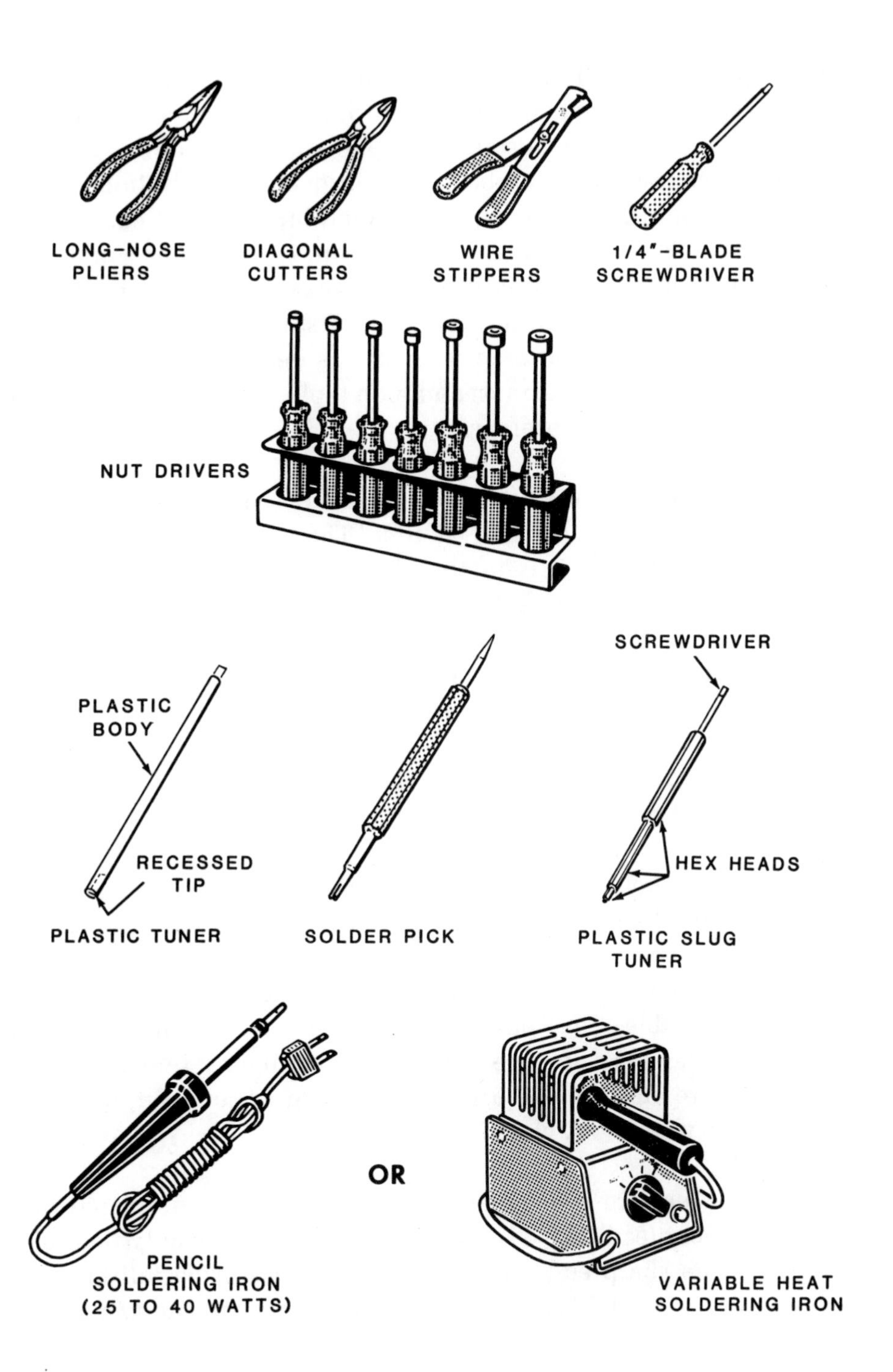

Figure 1
Typical electrical hand tools.

Any equipment used in testing a circuit can also be considered a hand tool. Test equipment includes multimeters, voltmeters, ammeters, ohmmeters, wattmeters, oscilloscopes, frequency counters, etc., as well as common test leads, probes, light indicators, and almost anything else that would be an aid in troubleshooting. The test equipment you use depends on what you are working on, and on what you are trying to do. It is enough, at this time, to simply define test equipment as hand tools. Like general purpose tools, test equipment should be used to perform the function for which it was designed. That is, it should be used properly. Unlike most common tools, its operation is not always obvious to the casual observer.

Knowing when and how to use electronic test equipment requires training and supervision, at least at first. The idea is to ensure that you are using it for what it is intended, and using it safely (this includes your safety, the circuit's safety, as well as the test equipment's safety). Proper use is important because the test equipment is expensive and very fragile. Test equipment that is not used properly can cause injuries, circuit damage, or at the very least, measurement errors.

ELECTRONICS AND SAFETY

By now, you should be aware that we are concerned about you working safely. And when it comes to electricity, we can't emphasize the idea of safety enough. In the electronics field, the primary dangers are from electrical shock and burns. As you will learn, certain electronic components are capable of exploding if they are improperly installed or defective. This presents a definite eye hazard, and in most industrial environments where electronic equipment is tested or serviced, everybody is required to wear safety glasses.

Accidents that are eye related can also occur when you clip a wire or component lead. The clipped portion can become a flying projectile, and with its sharp end, easily cause an injury, especially to the eye. The injury potential is not limited to just you, but could involve other people near you.

Some electronic components, even when operating properly, can generate enough heat to cause serious burns. For example, a 2-watt resistor can get very hot when it is operating near its capacity. For that reason, it is generally not mounted next to a circuit board, insulated wires, or other materials that can be damaged by heat.

When working with high voltage, a rubber mat should be used to isolate you from all conductors other than the circuit that you are working on. The mat helps prevent you from becoming grounded. This will reduce the possibility of current passing through your body should you accidentally touch an electrical "hot spot" in the equipment. As a further preventive measure, you should remove all jewelry before working on a "hot" (operating) circuit. Most jewelry is made of conductive metals and therefore conducts current. Gold and silver are two of the very best current conductors and could easily draw an arc from a high voltage source. There are many documented cases of a gold wedding band melting while still attached to a finger.

While on the subject of high voltages, here is one more safety tip. If possible, always work around high voltages with only one hand. This will ensure that if your are shocked, current can't pass from one hand, through your body, and out the other hand. It is possible for a very small amount of current to cause death, as shown in the Current Danger Chart in Figure 2.

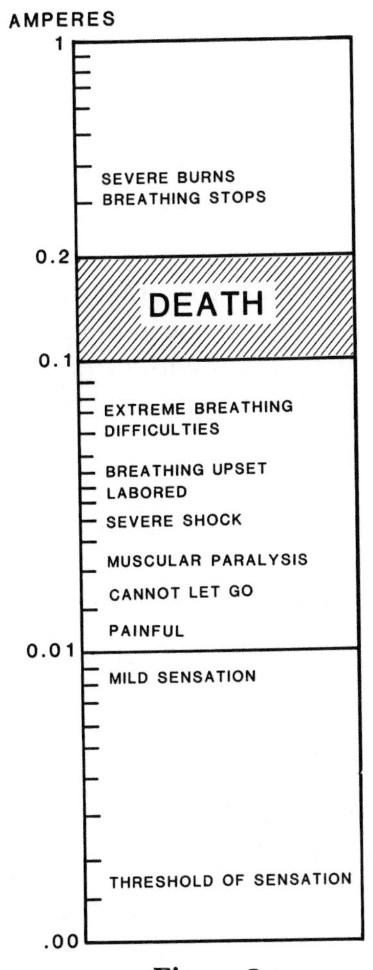

Figure 2
Current danger chart.

Finally, you should never work alone when servicing equipment that contains high voltages. Someone should be on hand to disable the power and provide first aid in case of an accident. It is possible to be shocked so severely that you will be unable to disengage yourself from the current source.

Although the following exercises do not involve high voltages, the safety tips we have just described should not be forgotten. Many of them still apply, and by learning to think **SAFETY** now, you may prevent a costly mistake some time in the future.

Exercise Format

The exercises are presented in the following format.

PURPOSE

Each exercise begins with one or more objectives. They state the goal of the exercise. You should keep these objectives in mind as you conduct the exercise.

MATERIAL REQUIRED

This section lists the components and other material you need to complete the exercise. Set these parts aside at the beginning of the exercise, so you won't have to look for them while you are performing the exercise. In addition to parts, this section lists the equipment needed to complete the exercise.

INTRODUCTION

This section tells you what you will be doing in the exercise. It may also be used to refresh your memory of specific topics covered in the corresponding unit.

PROCEDURE

This is a series of sequential steps that are the instructions for performing the exercise. The Procedure may contain questions regarding specific operations and their results. These serve to get you thinking about the operations you are performing. The Procedure is usually broken into several sections by supporting "Discussion" sections.

DISCUSSION

Each exercise has one or more "Discussions." Here, the procedure is reviewed, questions are answered, and important points are highlighted.

Exercise Schedule

We suggest that you perform the exercises in the following order. Your instructor may, however, follow a different schedule.

Exercises 1 and 2, after studying Unit 1.

Exercises 3, 4, and 5, after studying Unit 2.

Exercises 6 and 7, after studying Unit 3.

Exercises 8 and 9, after studying Unit 4.

Exercises 10 and 11, after studying Unit 5.

Exercises 12, 13, and 14, after studying Unit 6.

Exercise Parts List

This is a list of the parts for all of the exercises that you will perform in this course. The KEY numbers in the list correspond to the numbers in the part illustrations. Not all parts are illustrated, and those that are, may not be shown to scale. Some parts may be packaged in envelopes. Except for the initial parts check, keep these parts in their envelopes until they are called for in the exercise. In some cases, the parts may be hard to identify once they are separated from their packaging. When you finish an exercise where a hard-to-identify part is used, return the part to it's envelope, so the part can be identified the next time it is needed.

1/4-WATT, 5% RESISTORS

KEY No.	HEATH Part No.	QTY.	DESCRIPTION
A1	6-102-12	3	1000 Ω (brown-black-red-gold)
A1	6-103-12	2	10 kΩ (brown-black-orange-gold)
A1	6-104-12	1	100 kΩ (brown-black-yellow-gold)
A1	6-123-12	1	12 kΩ (brown-red-orange-gold)
A1	6-152-12	1	1500 Ω (brown-green-red-gold)
A1	6-153-12	1	15 kΩ (brown-green-orange-gold)
A1	6-202-12	1	2000 Ω (red-black-red-gold)
A1	6-203-12	1	20 kΩ (red-black-orange-gold)
A1	6-270-12	1	27 Ω (red-violet-black-gold)
A1	6-271-12	1	270 Ω (red-violet-brown-gold)
A1	6-273-12	1	27 kΩ (red-violet-orange-gold)
A1	6-303-12	1	30 kΩ (orange-black-orange-gold)
A1	6-309-12	1	3 Ω (orange-black-gold-gold)
A1	6-471-12	2	470 Ω (yellow-violet-brown-gold)
A1	6-562-12	1	5600 Ω (green-blue-red-gold)
A1	6-682-12	1	6800 Ω (blue-gray-red-gold)
A1	6-821-12	1	820 Ω (gray-red-brown-gold)

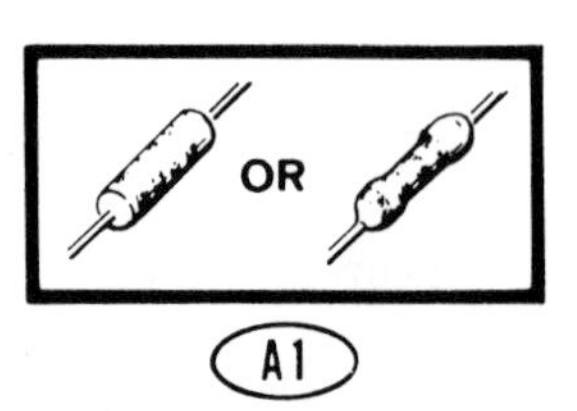

1/4-WATT, 1% RESISTORS

KEY No.	HEATH Part No.	QTY.	DESCRIPTION
A1	6-3831-12	1	3830 Ω (orange-gray-orange-brown-brown)
A1	6-4021-12	1	4020 Ω (yellow-black-red-brown-brown)
A1	6-4022-12	1	40.2 kΩ (yellow-black-red-red-brown)
A1	6-4532-12	1	45.3 kΩ (yellow-green-orange-red-brown)
A1	6-6041-12	1	6040 Ω (blue-black-yellow-brown-brown)

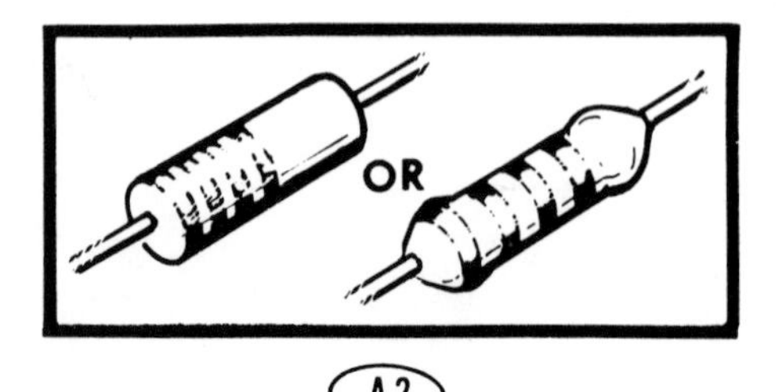

2-WATT, 5% RESISTOR

KEY No.	HEATH Part No.	QTY.	DESCRIPTION
A2	6-101-2	1	100 Ω (brown-black-brown-gold)

KEY No.	HEATH Part No.	QTY.	DESCRIPTION

MISCELLANEOUS PARTS

KEY No.	HEATH Part No.	QTY.	DESCRIPTION
B1	9-34	1	Thermistor
B2	9-67	1	Light dependent resistor (LDR)
B3	10-1141	1	1000 Ω, 0.75 W, 20% potentiometer
B3	10-1142	1	100 kΩ, 0.75 W, 20% potentiometer
B4	25-965	1	100 μF electrolytic capacitor
B5	45-601	1	10 mH coil
B6	56-89	2	Signal diode
B6	57-27	2	Silicon power diode
B7	60-2	1	Slide switch (DPDT)
B8	69-50	1	Relay
B9	69-121	1	Solenoid
	331-16	1	Solder
	340-18	18″	#22 nichrome wire (uninsulated)
	344-50	10′	Black #22 solid copper wire
	344-52	10′	Red #22 solid copper wire
	344-59	20′	White #22 solid copper wire
	346-44	6″	Black PVC tubing
B10	406-4	1	Compass
B11	407-719	1	1200 Ω, 200 μA meter movement
B12	412-87	2	6-volt, 50 mA lamp
B13	420-644	2	DC motor
B14	474-22	1	0.125″ × 0.125″ × 0.5″ magnet

B1

OR

B2

B3

B4

B5

NOTE: HEATH PART NUMBERS ARE STAMPED ON MOST DIODES.

OR

OR

OR

OR

OR

OR

B6

B7

B8

B9

B10

B11

B12

B13

B14

EXERCISE 1

Measuring Resistance

PURPOSE: Demonstrate the operation of an ohmmeter.

Demonstrate the proper method for "reading" the resistance of a banded resistor.

Illustrate the resistance characteristics of several different components.

Material Required

Trainer (ET-3100, ET-3600, or ET-1000)
Volt-Ohm-Milliammeter (VOM) or Ohmmeter.
All of the resistors supplied with the course.
1 6-volt lamp.
1 Light dependent resistor (LDR).
1 18″ length #22 nichrome wire.
White #22 copper hook-up wire.

Introduction

All materials have some level of resistance. You learned in Unit 1, that when dealing with electrical components, this resistance affects current flow and voltage drop. Before you can study current and voltage, however, you need to understand the resistive characteristics of several electrical components.

Therefore, in this exercise you will learn how to determine the resistance of a banded resistor by "reading" the band color code. You will also investigate the resistance characteristics of several different objects including a potentiometer (also called a pot or control), a lamp filament, and an LDR (light dependent resistor). To study these characteristics and to verify your banded resistor readings, you need to know how to use an ohmmeter. We'll cover that subject first.

OHMMETERS

An ohmmeter is a device that is used to measure resistance. Most ohmmeters can measure resistance from as low as a few tenths of an ohm to as high as several megohms. Figure E1-1 shows a set of scales from the face of a typical analog-type multi-function meter—digital meters don't use scales. The three bottom scales in this meter are used for AC and DC voltage and current measurements. The top scale is for resistance measurements.

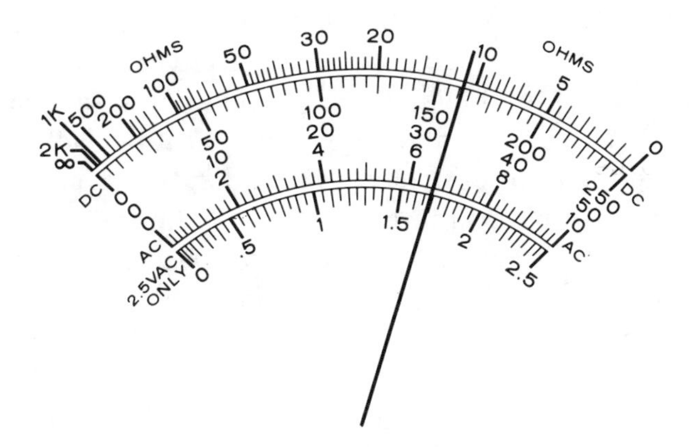

Figure E1-1
Meter scales from a typical multi-function meter.

Resistance is read in ohms from a nonlinear scale. Zero ohms is identified at one end of the scale, while infinite ohms is identified at the other end of the scale with the symbol for infinity. The term infinite is used, rather than some maximum value, because of the nonlinearity of the resistance scale.

An ohmmeter measures resistance by passing a current through the meter movement and the object being tested. The level of current passing through the circuit determines how far the meter pointer is deflected, and hence the resistance of the object. The current is supplied by a battery inside the meter. Digital meters operate in a similar fashion, only the meter movement is replaced by an electronic circuit that converts the current into a digital representation of the measured resistance.

When the meter leads on an analog meter are disconnected, the pointer indicates infinite resistance, because no current is passing through the meter. Digital meters usually show a random flashing display. Short the two meter leads together and the meter will indicate zero ohms. This is because there is no external resistance in the circuit, and maximum current is now passing through the meter. As the amount of resistance between the meter leads is increased, the meter current is reduced, and the meter pointer moves away from zero (or the digital display value increases).

Notice that the resistance range in the meter in Figure E1-1 is rather limited. Beyond 100 ohms, the resistance level is very hard to determine. To eliminate that problem, the ohmmeter has several range switch positions that are marked with a multiplication factor (1, 10, 100, etc.). You determine the resistance value displayed on the meter by multiplying the reading by the range factor. The meter in Figure E1-1 reads 11 ohms. If the range is set to 1, the reading is indeed 11 ohms. However, if the range is set to 100, then the meter is actually reading 11 × 100, or 1100 ohms.

Often, the range switch settings are identified with an "R ×" prefix. Thus, the 10 range would be labeled R × 10. This is a short-hand way of saying "multiply the meter reading by 10." Digital meters, on the other hand, always show the maximum resistance that can be measured on a particular range.

Most multi-function analog meters have a ZERO OHMS adjustment for the ohmmeter scale. It is used to set the zero deflection point of the meter pointer. It should be adjusted each time you change ranges on the meter. "Zero" the meter by first shorting the two test leads of the meter together. Then turn the ZERO OHMS knob or thumbwheel until the meter pointer is directly over the 0 ohms mark on the meter scale.

Many electronic-type analog ohmmeters also have a full-scale, or infinite, ohms adjustment. This is used to set the meter pointer over the infinity symbol on the meter scale when the test leads are disconnected. Often the zero and full-scale adjustments interact. This means you may have to repeat the two adjustments until you get the pointer properly aligned. You should check with the meter's Owner's Manual to determine the correct procedure.

Digital ohmmeters normally only have a ZERO OHMS adjustment. This is also set by shorting the two test leads together.

CAUTION: All portable ohmmeters and many AC powered meters use one or more batteries to supply meter current. Don't leave the test leads connected to a component or to each other for long periods of time. You will drain the battery. As a further precaution, switch the meter out of the ohms mode of operation when it isn't being used. This will eliminate the possibility of the leads shorting and draining the battery, or some internal meter circuitry draining the battery. One final precaution, DO NOT connect the ohmmeter to a circuit that has power applied. You may damage the meter movement on an analog meter. You may also damage the input circuitry on electronic and digital meters.

RESISTOR IDENTIFICATION

The resistance value of most low-wattage resistors is specified using a set of color bands painted on the body of the resistor. The bands are a code that tell you the value and the tolerance of that value. Depending upon the type of resistor, you will find four or five color bands painted on the body of the resistor. As a general rule, precision resistors, or resistors that are made to a nonstandard value use a five-band coding system. Common or general purpose resistors use the four-band coding system.

Figure E1-2 shows several typical resistor shapes and their banding. It also identifies the color code for each band of a resistor. Note that each color band represents a number. The first two or three, depending on the total number of bands, represent the first two or three digits in the resistor's value. The next band is used as a multiplier of that value. The last band specifies the value tolerance. For example, suppose a resistor had the four color bands in the sequence red, green, orange, and gold. What do you think the value would be?

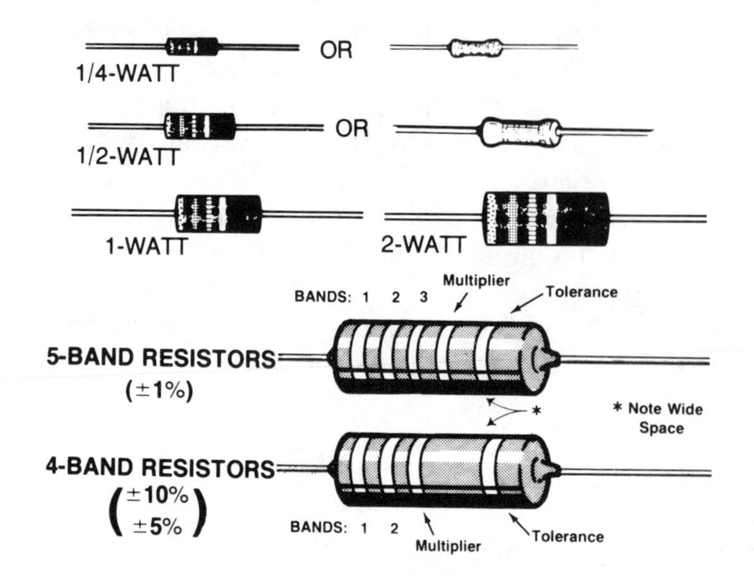

Band 1 1st Digit

Color	Digit
Black	0
Brown	1
Red	2
Orange	3
Yellow	4
Green	5
Blue	6
Violet	7
Gray	8
White	9

Band 2 2nd Digit

Color	Digit
Black	0
Brown	1
Red	2
Orange	3
Yellow	4
Green	5
Blue	6
Violet	7
Gray	8
White	9

Band 3 (if used) 3rd Digit

Color	Digit
Black	0
Brown	1
Red	2
Orange	3
Yellow	4
Green	5
Blue	6
Violet	7
Gray	8
White	9

Multiplier

Color	Multiplier
Black	1
Brown	10
Red	100
Orange	1,000
Yellow	10,000
Green	100,000
Blue	1,000,000
Silver	0.01
Gold	0.1

Resistance Tolerance

Color	Tolerance
Silver	± 10%
Gold	± 5%
Red	± 2%
Brown	± 1%
Green	± .5%
Blue	±.25%
Violet	± .1%
Gray	±.05%

Figure E1-2
Identifying banded resistor values.

Since there are only four bands, you know the resistor contains two value bands, one multiplier band, and one tolerance band. The red band equals 2, and the green band equals 5, so the basic value is 25. The orange multiplier band equals 1,000. Therefore, the resistor has a theoretical value of 25 × 1,000 = 25,000 Ω or 25 kΩ. Since the gold tolerance band equals ± 5%, the resistor could actually have a resistance between 23,750 Ω and 26,250 Ω.

Five-band resistors are "read" in the same manner, except in this case, there are three value bands. For example, the value for a resistor with the color band sequence blue, green, black, black, brown is determined in the following manner. The first three bands equal 650. The next band is a multiplier of 1. Therefore, the theoretical value is 650 × 1 = 650 Ω. The tolerance is ± 1%, so the resistor could actually have a resistance between 643.5 Ω and 656.5 Ω.

When you examine the resistors in this exercise, you will find that the tolerance band is separated from the three, or four, value and multiplier bands. This serves as a reference for determining from which direction, or end, you read the bands. You may find resistors with no tolerance band in some older electronic equipment. This used to be a method for indicating a tolerance of ± 20%. Today, however, manufacturers can produce resistors with a much tighter tolerance, so the ± 20% tolerance code has been discontinued.

Procedure

1. Refer to Figure E1-3 and calculate the theoretical resistance (CODED VALUE) for each resistor in the chart. Then determine the tolerance (TOL. %) for each resistor. You may refer to Figure E1-2 in the Exercise Introduction.

2. Make sure the your ohmmeter is calibrated as described in the Exercise Introduction. Then locate the banded resistors and select one of each value. You should now have a resistor representing each resistor in Figure E1-3.

FIRST COLOR	SECOND COLOR	THIRD COLOR	FOURTH COLOR	FIFTH COLOR	CODED VALUE	TOL. %	MEASURED VALUE
orange	black	gold	gold	—			
red	violet	black	gold	—			
brown	black	brown	gold	—			
red	violet	brown	gold	—			
yellow	violet	brown	gold	—			
gray	red	brown	gold	—			
brown	black	red	gold	—			
brown	green	red	gold	—			
red	black	red	gold	—			
orange	gray	orange	brown	brown			
yellow	black	red	brown	brown			
green	blue	red	gold	—			
blue	black	yellow	brown	brown			
blue	gray	red	gold	—			
brown	black	orange	gold	—			
brown	red	orange	gold	—			
brown	green	orange	gold	—			
red	black	orange	gold	—			
red	violet	orange	gold	—			
orange	black	orange	gold	—			
yellow	black	red	red	brown			
yellow	green	orange	red	brown			
brown	black	yellow	gold	—			

Figure E1-3

Resistor identification chart.

3. Measure the resistance of each resistor and record the value in Figure E1-3. Be sure to select a multiplier range on the ohmmeter that keeps the meter pointer (if you are using an analog meter) near the zero-end of the scale. That is the area that gives you the greatest resolution. Make sure you zero the meter each time you change ranges. Are the resistors within tolerance?

Discussion

By now, you should be familiar with the technique for reading the value of a banded resistor. You should also feel comfortable using an ohmmeter. By the way, did you remember to switch your meter out of the ohmmeter mode of operation when you finished?

When you determined the value of the resistors, did you notice that there were three different types? Two of the types were about the same size. However, the ones with four bands were 5% resistors, while the ones with five bands were 1% resistors. Keep in mind, though, the number of bands doesn't dictate the tolerance, the last band does. Also, the body color of a resistor has nothing to do with its value—different manufacturers often paint their resistors a different color.

The third type of resistor (the one that measured 100 Ω) was larger than the others. This is because it was a 2-watt resistor. The others were 1/4-watt resistors. Wattage is a function of how much power, and thus heat, a resistor can withstand without failing. Most resistors used in an electrical device like a radio or television are 1/4-watt in size because they don't have to handle high currents. When high currents are involved, larger resistors (2-watt, 5-watt, 10-watt, etc.) must be used to handle the heat that is generated.

All of the values that you measured should have fallen within the tolerances indicated for that resistor. Occasionally, a value may fall outside the tolerance range. However, this is usually caused by meter inaccuracies or difficulty in reading the high end of the scale of an analog meter.

Naturally, digital meters don't have scales to cause problems, but don't assume that what the meter indicates is necessarily the actual value of the component you are measuring. Digital meters have accuracy tolerances and they can drift out of calibration just like an analog-type meter.

In the next part of this exercise, you will examine the resistive characteristics of several other components.

Procedure Continued

4. If necessary, cut two 2-inch lengths of #22 copper hook-up wire and remove 1/4-inch of insulation from both ends of each piece. Clip a wire to each test lead of your ohmmeter.

5. The Trainer has two potentiometers (also known as controls or pots) with their leads brought to the breadboard surface through small connector blocks. An example is shown in Figure E1-4. Notice that the schematic symbol is also shown next to each pot. The two end blocks connect to the "resistive element" inside the pot, while the center block is connected to the "wiper" inside the pot.

   Set the ohmmeter to the appropriate range, R × 100 for analog meters or 2000 (2k) for digital meters. Then plug the ohmmeter into the end connector blocks of the 1 kΩ pot. What is the resistance? .986 K Ω.

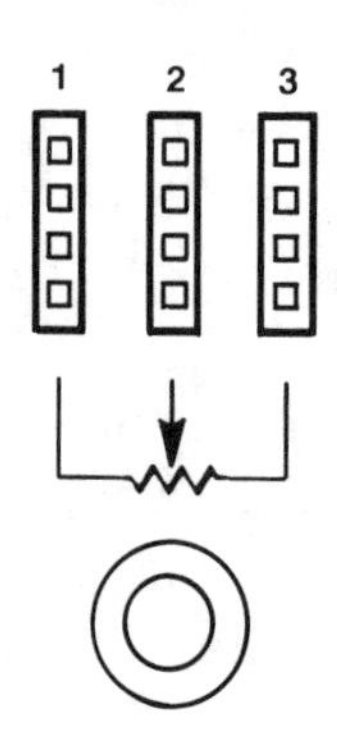

Figure E1-4
Trainer potentiometer.

6. Turn the pot knob fully clockwise (CW) and fully counter clockwise (CCW). Leave the knob in the CCW position. Did the resistance change? no .988KΩ

7. Pull one of the test leads and plug it into the center (wiper) connector block of the pot. The resistance is .181K Ω. What does this tell you about the position of the wiper inside the pot?

___

___

8. Slowly turn the pot knob CW and observe the resistance. When the pot is fully CW, the resistance is 1.168k Ω. What does this tell you about the position of the wiper? ______________________

____

Discussion

The banded resistors you tested in the first part of this exercise are also called fixed resistors—their resistance is essentially fixed, although they may change a little with changes in temperature. The pot is an example of a variable resistor. It's not, however, a variable resistor because its resistive element changes. You saw in step 6 that turning the knob had no effect on the ohmmeter reading. Rather, it is a variable resistor because you can "tap" a portion of the resistance through the pot wiper.

In step 7, you shifted one of the ohmmeter test leads to the wiper connector block. This may or may not have changed the ohmmeter reading, depending on which lead was shifted. Turning the pot knob caused the resistance to change either up or down. The change in resistance occurs because the wiper controls how much of the resistive element is in the circuit.

The resistance measured when the wiper is full CW or full CCW is a function of the construction of the pot. Some pots actually short the wiper to the leads where they attach to the element. Other pots, like those in the Trainer, use a method of construction where the wiper may not quite reach the ends of the resistive element. As a result, the minimum wiper resistance is often several ohms greater than zero, and the maximum wiper resistance is often several ohms less than the maximum resistance of the element.

The resistance you measured in step 5 is between 800 Ω and 1200 Ω*. That's because the pot has a tolerance of ±20%. This is typical of most pots, because it helps to keep the cost to manufacture down, and because most pots are used to "fine tune" a circuit where only a portion of the total resistance is used.

* The one exception is the later versions of the ET-3600 Analog Trainer. They have a 180 Ω or 210 Ω, 5 W, 10% fixed-value resistor wired in series with the wiper and connector block. As a result, the high resistance range is between 962 Ω and 1431 Ω, while the low resistance range is between 162 Ω and 231 Ω, rather than 0 Ω.

Procedure Continued

9. Refer to Figure E1-5. This is a diagram of the ET-3100 breadboarding area. It is similar to that found on the ET-3600 and ET-1000 Trainers. Notice the large connector block in the center of the trainer. This is where you will construct the circuits in these exercises. The connector block is made up of many small connector groups. Each connector group has five holes that are electrically shorted together vertically. The connector groups are isolated from each other horizontally. To see what we mean, insert your ohmmeter test leads into two adjacent holes in the large connector block and measure the resistance. If the holes are vertically adjacent, and in the same connector group, the meter will show zero resistance. If the two holes are horizontally adjacent, the meter will show infinite resistance. By the same token, if the holes are vertically adjacent, in two different connector groups, the meter will show infinite resistance.

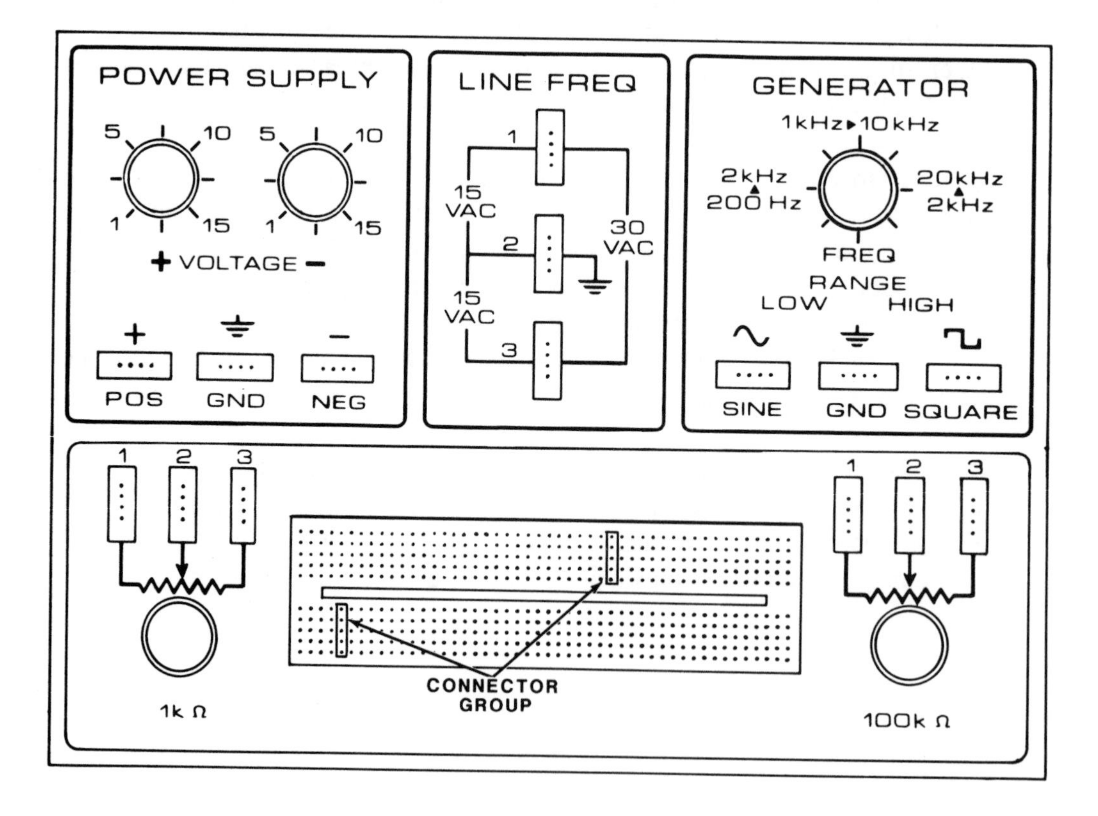

Figure E1-5
The ET-3100 Trainer breadboarding area.

10. If necessary, cut an 18-inch length of copper hook-up wire and remove 1/4-inch of insulation from each end of the wire. Plug the wire into opposite ends of the large connector block. Now plug the 18-inch length of #22 nichrome wire into opposite ends of the large connector block, but in different connector groups than the copper wire. Plug your ohmmeter into the same connector groups as the copper wire. The resistance of the copper wire is .2 Ω. Now plug your ohmmeter into the same connector groups as the nichrome wire. The resistance of the nichrome wire is 1.7 Ω. Leave one lead of the meter plugged into the large connector block and touch the other lead to the middle of the nichrome wire. The resistance is 1.1 Ω. What are you conclusions? longer the wire more rest.

11. Locate the light dependent resistor (LDR) and plug its leads into two different connector groups in the large connector block. Plug your ohmmeter into the same connector groups and measure the resistance of the LDR. Its resistance is 2.000KΩ. Now cover the LDR with you hand. The resistance is now 20 K Ω. Vary the amount of light falling on the LDR and observe the resistance. What are your conclusions? Less light more resistance
nichrom is linear in resist.

12. Locate the 6-volt lamp and plug it into the large connector block. Its resistance is 14.5 Ω.
12.9

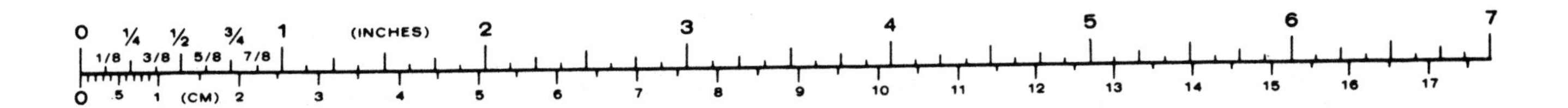

Discussion

In this part of the exercise, you learned that different components or elements have different resistances or resistance characteristics. Unless you have an extremely sensitive ohmmeter, the copper wire you measured had a resistance of 0 Ω. As the chart in Figure E1-6 shows, #22 gauge copper wire actually has a typical resistance of 0.0161 ohms per foot. The #22 nichrome wire should have measured about 1.5 Ω since the manufacturer specifies a typical resistance of 1 ohm per foot. However, for such a small sample of wire, its resistance could vary between 0.5 and 2 Ω because of tolerance errors, wire impurities, and actual wire diameter. Figure E1-7 shows the ratio of resistance for different types of metal compared to copper. You can see that silver has approximately the same resistance as copper, while nichrome has 60 times the resistance.

The resistive element in the LDR has a great deal more resistance than copper wire. It also has another characteristic that is quite different from copper wire. The resistance changes with light. A bright light will cause the resistance to fall to about 4,000 Ω while an absence of light will raise the resistance to over 20,000,000 Ω. You probably noticed resistance changes between 10,000 Ω and 190,000 Ω.

The last component you tested is a 6-volt lamp. It's resistance is about 15 Ω, ± 5 Ω. Here you are measuring the filament of a lamp, and the resistance can vary quite a bit because of the inaccuracies of attaching the filament wire to its supports. If you measured a resistance greater than 20 Ω, then you know your ohmmeter contains a large current source. That current was heating the lamp filament, and thus, raising the filament resistance. You will learn in a later exercise that the resistance of the filament will change a great amount when the lamp is lit.

Procedure Continued

13. Remove the parts from the Trainer connector block and save them for future exercises.

14. If you haven't already done so, switch the meter out of the ohmmeter operating mode.

15. This completes the first exercise. Proceed to the next exercise where you will study the characteristics of the two other circuit variables current and voltage, and their relationship to resistance in Ohm's Law.

NUMBER	DIAMETER IN MILS	AREA IN CIRCULAR MILS	OHMS PER 1000 FT	
			COPPER * 68°F	COPPER * 167°F
0000	460	211,600	.049	.0596
000	410	167,800	.0618	.0752
00	365	133,100	.078	.0948
0	325	105,500	.0983	.1195
1	289	83,690	.1239	.151
2	258	66,370	.1563	.190
3	229	52,640	.1970	.240
4	204	41,740	.2485	.302
5	182	33,100	.3133	.381
6	162	26,250	.395	.481
7	144	20,820	.498	.606
8	128	16,510	.628	.764
9	114	13,090	.792	.963
10	102	10,380	.999	1.215
11	91	8,234	1.260	1.532
12	81	6,540	1.588	1.931
13	72	5,178	2.003	2.44
14	64	4,107	2.525	3.07
15	57	3,257	3.184	3.87
16	51	2,583	4.016	4.88
17	45.3	2,048	5.06	6.16
18	40.3	1,624	6.39	7.77
19	35.9	1,288	8.05	9.79
20	32.0	1,022	10.15	12.35
21	28.5	810	12.8	15.6
22	25.4	642	16.1	19.6
23	22.6	510	20.4	24.8
24	20.1	404	25.7	31.2
25	17.9	320	32.4	39.4
26	15.9	254	40.8	49.6
27	14.2	202	51.5	62.6
28	12.6	160	64.9	78.9
29	11.3	126.7	81.8	99.5
30	10.0	100.5	103.2	125.5
31	8.93	79.7	130.1	158.2
32	7.95	63.2	164.1	199.5
33	7.08	50.1	207	252
34	6.31	39.8	261	317
35	5.62	31.5	329	400
36	5.00	25.0	415	505
37	4.45	19.8	523	636
38	3.96	15.7	660	802
39	3.53	12.5	832	1012
40	3.15	9.9	1049	1276

Figure E1-6

Copper wire gauge and resistance chart.

ALUMINUM	1.59
BRASS	4.40
GOLD	1.38
IRON	6.67
LEAD	12.76
NICHROME	60.
NICKEL	7.73
PLATINUM	5.80
SILVER	0.92
STEEL	8.62
TIN	8.2
TUNGSTEN	3.2
ZINC	3.62

Figure E1-7

Ratio of resistance of metals as compared to copper.

EXERCISE 2

Ohm's Law

PURPOSE: Demonstrate the operation of an ammeter.

Demonstrate the operation of a voltmeter.

Show how voltage can be calculated knowing current and resistance.

Show how current can be calculated knowing voltage and resistance.

Show how resistance can be calculated knowing voltage and current.

Show how a change in voltage, current, or resistance in a circuit can affect the characteristics of the circuit.

Show how power can be calculated knowing voltage and current.

Material Required

Trainer.
Small soldering iron (25-35 watt).
VOM or individual DC volt, ohm, and DC milliamp meters.
1 100 Ω resistor.
1 1000 Ω resistor.
1 Thermistor.
1 6-volt lamp.
White #22 copper hook-up wire.

Introduction

In the last exercise, you studied the characteristics of resistance and the operation of the ohmmeter. As you know, resistance is only one of the variables that make up Ohm's Law. This exercise completes your introduction to Ohm's Law by showing you the characteristics of the other two variables, voltage and current. As part of this study, you will also learn how to use a voltmeter and an ammeter, beginning with the ammeter.

AMMETERS

Ammeters are used to measure current. Actually, most of the meters that you will use are called milliammeters. That's because they are designed for electrical circuits where the currents are quite low. Recall that a milliampere is 1/1000 ampere. A milliammeter normally measures current in thousandths of amperes. The full measurement range is typically from less than a tenth of a milliampere to about 1000 milliamperes.

Unlike the ohmmeter, the scale for a milliammeter is linear. Figure E2-1 shows a set of scales from a typical multi-function meter, or as it is commonly called, a VOM. The scale marked DC is used when measuring current. Although this meter can only measure DC current, some meters can also measure AC current. Those meters add a separate scale for that function.

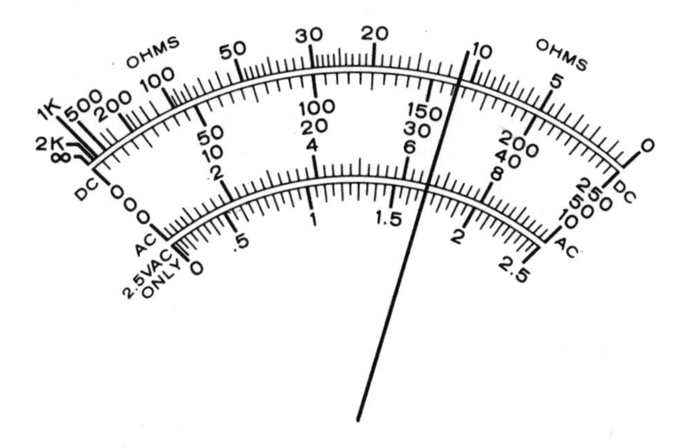

Figure E2-1
Meter scales from a typical multi-function meter.

The 0 to 10 and 0 to 50 scale ranges in the figure are used on this meter for current measurement. Thus, when you select the 1, 10, and 100 milliampere ranges use the 0 to 10 range scale and interpret the reading to match the range. For example, a reading of 6.5 on the 100 range is equal to 65 milliamperes. When you use the .05 and 500 milliampere ranges use the 0 to 50 range scale, and again, interpret the reading. Digital meters, of course, don't have scales, since they don't use an analog-type meter movement.

Recall from Unit 1 that when you use a milliammeter (ammeter), it is placed in the current path of the circuit. The negative test lead is connected to the ground, or negative, side of the circuit. The positive test lead is connected to the positive side of the circuit. Many meters have a polarity switch. This allows you to change the polarity of the test leads without moving the leads. Other meters have an automatic polarity sensing circuit that changes the polarity for you.

To keep the discussion simple, we will call all current measuring meters ammeters whether they are designed to measure amps or milliamps.

VOLTMETERS

The last meter is the voltmeter. Its scales are marked DC, AC, and 2.5 VAC in Figure E2-1. While the scales are essentially linear, notice that the two AC scales are slightly different in the way the scale graduations are handled. They are compressed on the low end of the scale to compensate for the AC components inside the meter. (You'll learn more about those components in Unit 6.) Because of these graduation differences, you must remember to use the correct scale when measuring voltage.

As with the ammeter, each scale can accommodate several ranges. You may have to interpret the reading depending on the range you select. The one exception is the 2.5 VAC scale. It is only used with the 2.5 VAC range.

Recall that you use the voltmeter to measure voltage rise and voltage drop. To measure a voltage rise, you connect the meter across the power supply leads. To measure a voltage drop, you connect the meter across the circuit component leads. In either instance, you must make sure to connect the negative test lead to the negative or ground side, and positive test lead to the positive side. As with the ammeter, the voltmeter may have a polarity switch or automatic polarity sensing.

Procedure

1. Make sure Trainer power is switched off. Then refer to Figure E2-2 and construct the circuit shown. If necessary, prepare a 6-inch length of hook-up wire to connect one lead of the 100 Ω resistor to the positive (+) connector block of the Trainer Power Supply. Then use the two 2-inch pieces of hook-up wire you prepared in the first exercise to connect the ammeter to the ground (GND) connector block of the Trainer Power Supply and the other lead of the resistor. Note that on the ET-1000 Trainer, the positive connector block is on the right side next to the + VOLTS knob, and the ground connector block is on the left side of the large connector block, and it is identified by a ground symbol.

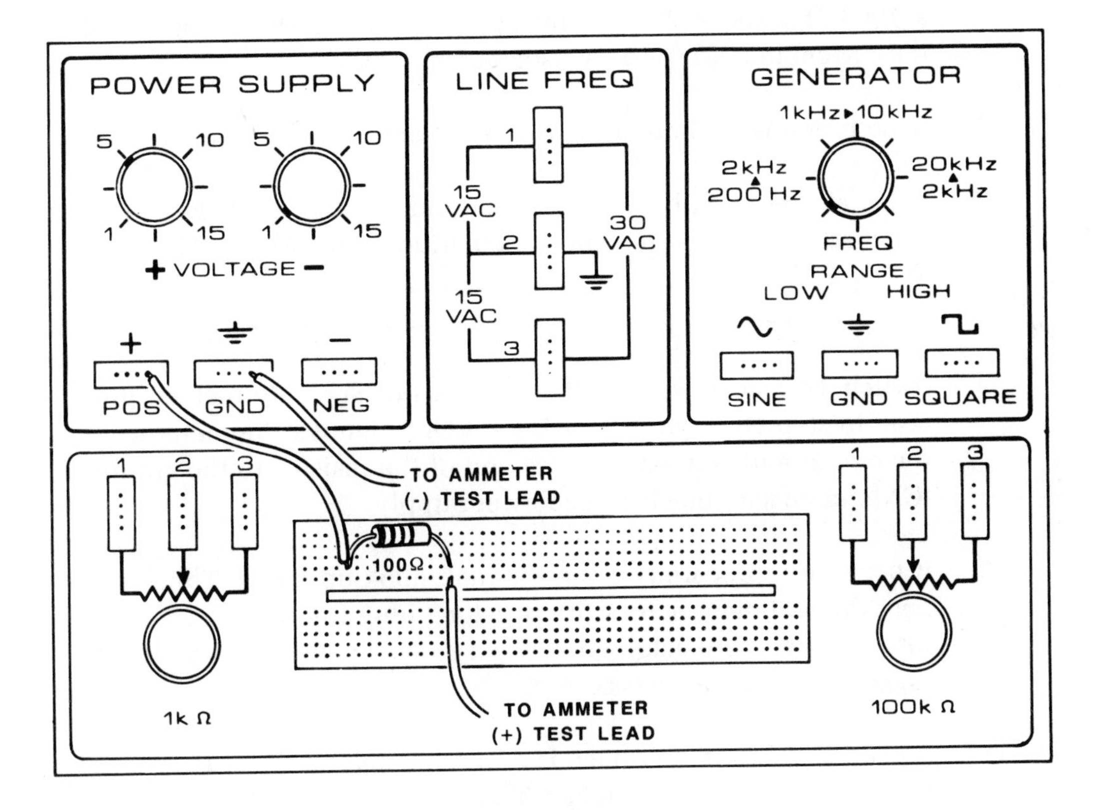

Figure E2-2
Current test circuit.

2. Turn the negative (−) Power Supply knob fully CCW. Then turn the positive (+) Power Supply knob to align its mark with the number 5. This will give you an output voltage close to 5 V.

3. Make sure your ammeter is in the DC current mode. Then set the input range to its highest level.

NOTE: You should **always** set your meter to its highest range when you are measuring an unknown current or voltage. That way, you reduce the chance of damaging the meter movement or input circuitry. After you apply the current or voltage to the meter, you can select a lower range to get a usable reading.

4. Switch Trainer power on and note the meter reading. Did the pointer move down-scale, below zero? If so, you either have the test leads reversed or the polarity switch is reversed. Fix the problem before you proceed. Now select a range that gives you a usable reading. The current is ______ mA.

5. Calculate the supply voltage. It should be ______ V.

6. Switch Trainer power off and replace the 100 Ω resistor with a 1000 Ω resistor. When you apply power to the circuit, will the current increase or decrease? ______

7. Switch Trainer on and measure the current. It is ______ mA.

8. Calculate the supply voltage. It should be ______ V. Does this calculated voltage match your calculation in step 5? Explain: ______

9. Switch Trainer power off. If you are using separate meters, proceed to step 10. If you are using a VOM, remove the meter from the circuit and connect the free end of the resistor to the ground (GND) connector block of the Power Supply.

10. If necessary, prepare two more 2-inch hook-up wires. Then connect the voltmeter across the resistor—plug the meter test leads into the two connector groups occupied by the resistor leads. Make sure the polarity is correct.

11. Since you know the voltage is approximately 5 V, set the meter range to measure 5 V. Switch Trainer power on. The voltage is ______ V. How does this compare with your calculations, and why are there any differences? ______

Discussion

The current you measured in the circuit using the 100 Ω resistor should have been close to 50 mA. This is supported by Ohm's Law. If you assume the Power Supply voltage is 5 V, then:

$$\text{CURRENT} = \frac{\text{VOLTAGE}}{\text{RESISTANCE}}$$

$$\text{CURRENT} = \frac{5\ \text{V}}{100\ \Omega}$$

$$\text{CURRENT} = 0.05\ \text{A}$$

$$\text{CURRENT} = 50\ \text{mA}$$

After you measured the current, you were able to calculate the Power Supply voltage using Ohm's Law. As an example, if the measured current was 46.9 mA, or 0.0469 A, then:

$$\text{VOLTAGE} = \text{CURRENT} \times \text{RESISTANCE}$$

$$\text{VOLTAGE} = 0.0469\ \text{A} \times 100\ \Omega$$

$$\text{VOLTAGE} = 4.69\ \text{V}$$

Changing the resistor value in the circuit to 1000 Ω reduced the current to about 10% of the original current. The Power Supply voltage didn't change. However, the calculated voltage may have changed. If that happened, it's because there was not an exact tenfold change in the circuit resistance. Remember, both resistors have a ± 5% tolerance in their specified value.

Finally, you measured the voltage and probably found that it was close to what you calculated, but not exactly the same. Again, this is primarily due to the tolerance of the resistor. However, there are two other factors that will also affect the calculated versus measured voltage of the circuit. The first factor is a combination of meter circuit tolerance and linearity. **Tolerance**, of course, is a function of the tolerance of the parts that make up the meter circuit—resistors, switch resistance, and meter movement for an analog meter; and resistors, capacitors, switch resistance, and display conversion circuitry for a digital meter.

Linearity is a function of how the meter movement or digital display circuitry respond to different levels of input current for a given range. The second factor is the loading effect the meter has on the circuit being tested. **Load** is a term that's used for the resistance that is added to the circuit being tested by the circuit inside the meter. You'll learn more about these factors in later units, as you build on your understanding of the concepts of electricity. For now, just remember that a meter cannot give you a precise reading for a specific value. However, the error is generally insignificant, when compared to what you are trying to determine about a circuit value.

Refer to Figure E2-3. It is a schematic drawing of the circuit you have been studying. Notice that it shows both an ammeter and a voltmeter in the circuit. Naturally, if you have been working with a VOM, only one meter can be attached at one time. In addition, the circuit power supply is labeled with a plus (+) symbol to identify the positive Trainer Power Supply connector and a minus (−) symbol to identify the **ground** Trainer Power Supply connector. **Don't** use the negative Trainer Power Supply connector by mistake.

In the next part of the exercise, you will replace the fixed resistor with the 1000 Ω (1 kΩ) pot on the Trainer.

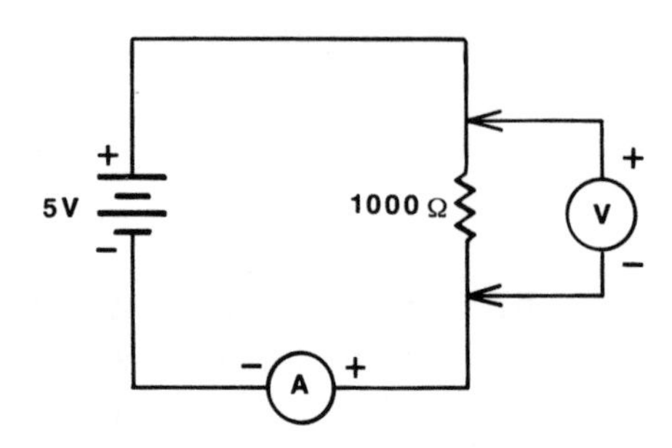

Figure E2-3
Schematic diagram of the test circuit using a fixed resistor.

Procedure Continued

12. Connect your voltmeter to the positive and ground Trainer Power Supply connectors. Adjust the Power Supply for +5 V. Then disconnect the voltmeter.

13. Switch Trainer power off. Then refer to Figure E2-4 and replace the fixed resistor in your circuit with the 1000 Ω pot on the Trainer. Notice that one side of the Power Supply is connected to the pot wiper. The other side of the Power Supply is connected to the ammeter, which in turn, is connected to one end of the pot resistive element. If you are using a VOM, install it as an ammeter at this time. Regardless of the type of ammeter you are using, set it to measure current in the range of 0 to 20 milliamps.

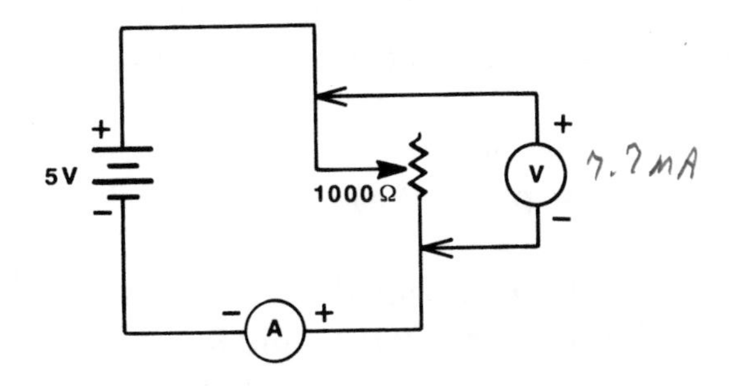

Figure E2-4
Schematic diagram of the test circuit using a pot.

14. Turn the pot wiper to about the center of its rotation. Switch Trainer power on. The current passing through the pot is 7.7 mA.

15. Knowing the supply voltage and circuit current, calculate the resistance of the pot. The resistance is 671 Ω.

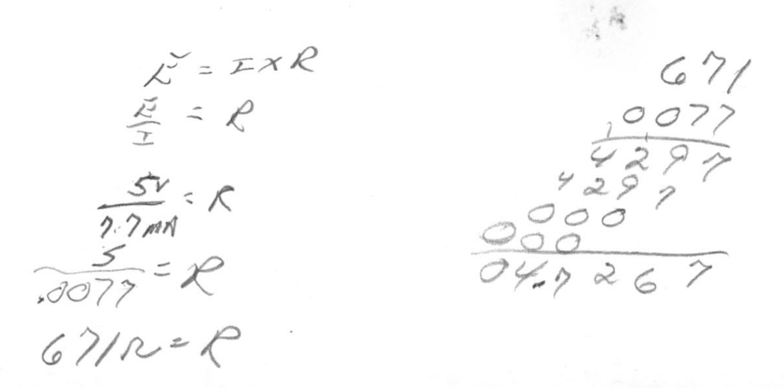

16. Switch Trainer power off. If you are using separate meters, connect your voltmeter to the Trainer Power Supply. If you are using a VOM, remove the ammeter from the circuit, switch it to the voltmeter mode of operation, and connect it to the Trainer Power Supply. Make sure you close the current path that you opened when you removed the ammeter. Switch Trainer power on.

17. Adjust the Power Supply for + 10 V.

18. Switch Trainer power off. Then remove the wires going to the pot. Measure the resistance of the pot. It is 668 Ω. How does this compare to the resistance you calculated in step 15?

____

____

NOTE: When you measure the resistance of a part, you must **always** isolate it from any other circuit components. If you don't those components may cause a loading effect and give a false reading.

19. Carefully reconstruct your circuit so you don't change the position of the pot wiper, or the Power Supply knob.

20. Now that you have measured the resistance and reset the voltage, calculate the new current. It should be 14.97 mA.

21. Knowing what the current should be, set the ammeter to the proper range and switch Trainer power on. The current is now 14.9 mA. Is the current what you expected? Explain your results: ____

____

Discussion

In the first section of the exercise, you determined voltage using a fixed resistance and a measured current. In this section, you first determined resistance using an measured voltage and a measured current. Then you determined current using a measured voltage and a measured resistance.

In step 14, you placed an unknown resistance in the circuit. After measuring the voltage and current, you calculated the resistance. For example, with a voltage of 5 V and a current of say 13.63 mA, then by Ohm's Law:

$$\text{RESISTANCE} = \frac{\text{VOLTAGE}}{\text{CURRENT}}$$

$$\text{RESISTANCE} = \frac{5\ \text{V}}{0.01363\ \text{A}}$$

$$\text{RESISTANCE} = 367\ \Omega$$

Your current, and hence the resistance, is probably different but close to these values. When you measured the resistance of the pot, it should have been close to your calculated value. Again, keep in mind that your test instruments (all three of them) will affect your results.

After you determined the pot's resistance, we had you double the supply voltage. That should have been a clue that the current would also double. Remember, current and voltage are directly proportional. If one is doubled, the other must also double, assuming the resistance is constant. Your calculations should have verified that concept. Depending on how accurate your instruments are, the current you measured should have also doubled.

The last part of the exercise will touch on one other general characteristic of resistive elements—how their resistance changes with temperature.

Procedure Continued

22. Switch the Trainer off and remove all of the wires and components.

23. Plug the two leads of the thermistor into separate connector groups of the large connector block on the Trainer. Connect your ohmmeter to the leads. The resistance is ________Ω.

24. Now hold the thermistor between your thumb and index finger. You should notice a small change in its resistance. The change will occur gradually as your fingers heat the thermistor. Does the resistance reading increase or decrease? ________________

25. Heat a low wattage soldering iron. Hold the iron against the **black** edge of the thermistor. Do not hold the iron against the silver part of the thermistor. That is a coating of solder used to hold the thermistor leads in place. Continue to heat the thermistor until the resistance reading stops changing. That will happen at about 20 Ω. The resistance is now ________Ω.

26. Remove the iron from the thermistor. Unplug the iron and set it aside to cool. Also, let the thermistor cool before you proceed.

27. Switch the Trainer on and set the Power Supply to +6 V. Switch the Trainer off and construct the thermistor circuit shown in Figure E2-5. Notice that the schematic symbol for a thermistor is a circled resistor and the letter T. Often, the resistor symbol inside the circle will have an arrow through it to show that the resistance is variable.

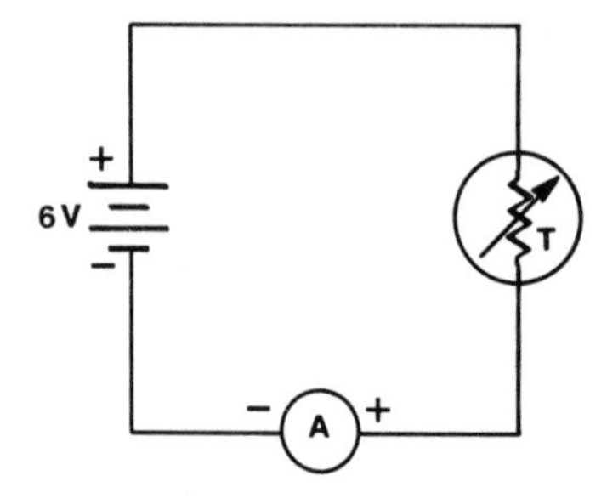

Figure E2-5
Thermistor circuit.

28. Switch the Trainer on and observe the ammeter. Is the current increasing or decreasing? ________ Hold the thermistor. What happens to the current? Let go, and observe the current. When it stops changing, or when the current exceeds 150 mA, switch the Trainer off. Carefully touch the thermistor. Is it hot? ________ Can you explain why? ________

____

29. After the thermistor cools down, remove the thermistor circuit from Trainer and construct the lamp circuit shown in Figure E2-6. Switch the Trainer on and measure the current through the lamp. It is 38.8 mA. What does the lamp filament look like? glows

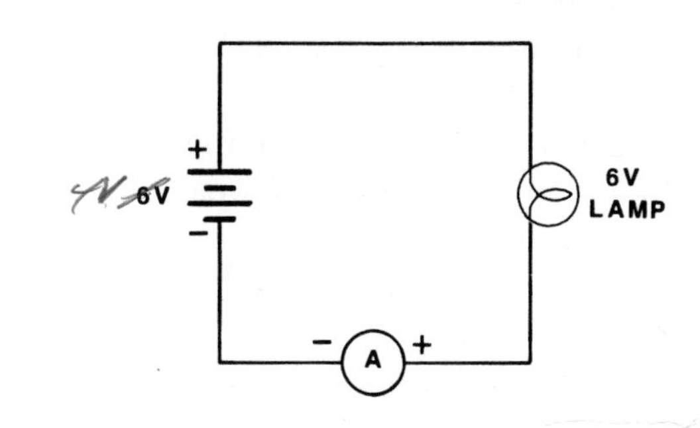

Figure E2-6

Lamp circuit.

P = I × E
P = 38.8·4

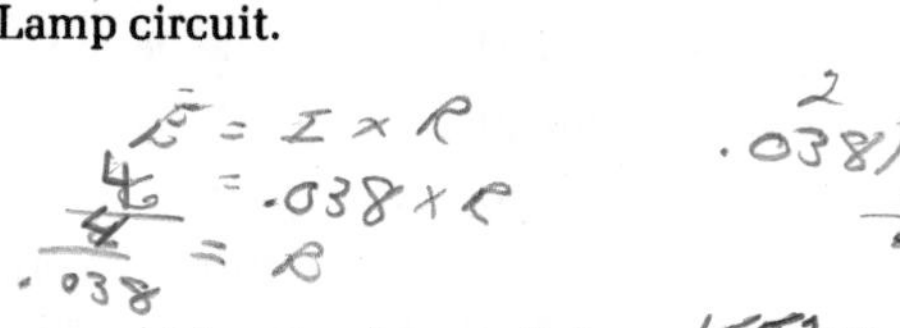
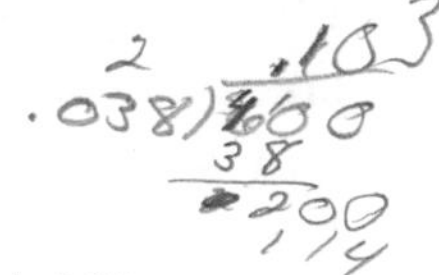

30. Calculate the power dissipated by the lamp. It is .1552 W.

31. Calculate the resistance of the lamp. It is 103 Ω.

32. Turn the Trainer Power Supply knob fully CCW. The current is 20 mA. What does the filament look like now? Dimmer

33. Measure the supply voltage. It is 1.252 V. Calculate the resistance of the lamp. It is 62.6 Ω.

34. Switch Trainer power off. Measure the resistance of the lamp. It is 14.2 Ω. How do you account for the large difference between measured and calculated resistances? Heat increase resistances

Discussion

The resistive elements in most components maintain a relatively constant resistance because they operate within a narrow temperature range. Other resistive elements produce large changes in resistance, with changes in temperature. Thermistors and lamps fall into that category.

The thermistor you tested has a typical resistance of 120 Ω. When you held it, the resistance decreased a small amount. Later, when you heated it with the soldering iron, the resistance fell to about 20 Ω. What you found was that with an increase in temperature, there was a decrease in resistance. Thus, you can say that the thermistor you tested has a **negative temperature coefficient**.

When you applied a 6-volt potential to the thermistor, the current slowly increased. Recall, that when current passes through a resistance, some of the energy is converted into heat. In the case of your thermistor, that heat caused the resistance to decrease. As the the resistance decreased, the current increased. This "snowball" effect caused the current to continue to increase until the Trainer Power Supply was pushed to its full capacity, or you switched off the power.

When you touched the thermistor, as it was heating, the current decreased a small amount. That's because you were acting as a "heatsink" and you lowered the temperature of the thermistor. As a result, the resistance increased causing the current to decrease. When you let go, the thermistor proceeded to heat and the current again increased.

The lamp filament is an example of a positive temperature coefficient resistive element. Apply a voltage to the lamp and the resulting current causes the filament to heat. As the filament heats, its resistance increases. A point is quickly reached where the current can no longer make the filament any hotter. For example, if the filament does get hotter, the resistance will increase. That increased resistance causes the current to decrease. Decrease the current, and the filament cools down. A cooler filament has less resistance, so more current flows, and the filament gets hotter. This heating and cooling process occurs over a very narrow range, and so in effect, you can say the current and resistance have stabilized.

The amount of voltage applied to the lamp determines at what point the current and resistance stabilize. When you applied about 1.2 V to the lamp, the current and resistance stabilized at a low level, the amount of heat in the filament was relatively low, and it barely glowed. Increasing the voltage to 6 V caused the current and resistance to increase, the filament heat increased, and it glowed brightly.

Thus, the voltage level, in effect, controls the brightness of the filament. If you exceed the specified voltage level, you will either shorten the life of the lamp or cause it to burn out immediately.

The power rating for the lamp is 0.3 W at 6 V. Your power dissipation calculation should have been close to that value. For example, with a voltage of 6 V, and a measured lamp current of 49.3 mA, then:

$$\text{POWER} = \text{CURRENT} \times \text{VOLTAGE}$$

$$\text{POWER} = 0.0493\ \text{A} \times 6\ \text{V}$$

$$\text{POWER} = 0.2958\ \text{W}$$

Your current, and hence the wattage, is probably different but close to these values.

Procedure Continued

35. This completes Exercise 2 and the exercises for Unit 1. Remove all of the wire and components from the Trainer, and save them for future exercises. Clean-up your work area.

36. Return to Unit 1 and complete the Unit Examination.

EXERCISE 3

Series Circuits

PURPOSE: Show that voltage rise equals the sum of the voltages dropped in a series circuit.

Show that current is constant throughout a series circuit.

Show how a change in one electrical characteristic of a series circuit can affect the other electrical characteristics.

Material Required

Trainer.
Small soldering iron (25-35 watt).
Solder.
VOM or individual DC volt, ohm, and DC ammeters.
1 100 Ω resistor.
3 1000 Ω resistor.
2 6-volt lamp.
1 Slide switch.
White #22 copper hook-up wire.

Introduction

By now, you understand the basic characteristics of a resistive element and you can use Ohm's Law to calculate an unknown electrical value when given two known values. Unit 2 introduced you to the concept of series and parallel circuits. In this exercise, you will have an opportunity to build several different series circuits and observe their operating characteristics. You will be asked, at different times, to measure voltage, current, or resistance within those circuits. You will also be asked to use those measurements to determine unknown values of voltage, current, or resistance.

Procedure

1. Refer to Figure E3-1 and prepare the slide switch as follows. Cut two 2" lengths of wire and remove 1/4" of insulation from each end. Crimp one end of each wire to the switch as shown. Then solder the connections.

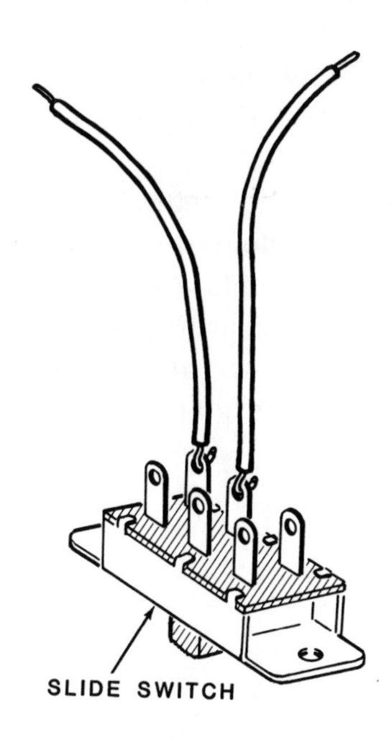

Figure E3-1
Soldering leads to the switch.

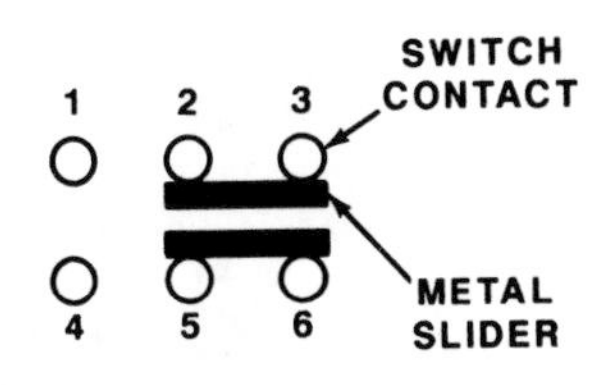

Figure E3-2
Illustration of a double-pole, double-throw, slide switch.

The slide switch you just prepared is called a double-pole, double-throw (DPDT) switch. The switch gets its name from the fact that there are two isolated sets of contacts (double-pole) and two possible "closed" positions for each set of contacts (double-throw). Figure E3-2 shows how the switch works.

Contacts 1, 2, and 3 form one set of poles, while contacts 4, 5, and 6 form the second set of poles. Each set of poles has a metal slider, or shorting bar, that's attached to the switch slide. When the switch is positioned as shown in the figure, contacts 2 and 3 are shorted together, and contacts 5 and 6 are shorted together. Electrically speaking, contacts 2 and 3 are "closed," and contacts 1 and 2 are "open." Slide the switch lever to the other end, and contacts 1 and 2 close, while contacts 2 and 3 open. You can verify this operation with an ohmmeter.

2. Connect your ohmmeter to the switch lugs with the wires. Slide the switch lever back and forth, and note the meter response. When the lever is positioned over the lugs with wires, the circuit is closed. When the lever is positioned away from the lugs with the wires, the circuit is open.

   This switch will be used to open and close the circuits you will build in this and other exercises. Note that although the switch has two sets of contacts, we will only show one set in this, and the following schematics, since you are only using the one set.

3. Refer to the 1-resistor series circuit schematic in Figure E3-3. You are familiar with the symbol for a voltage potential (power supply) and a resistor. The other symbol represents a switch. The switch is shown in its open position. Now make sure the Trainer power is switched off, and build the circuit shown in Figure E3-3. Move the switch lever to its open position. This opens the current path in the circuit.

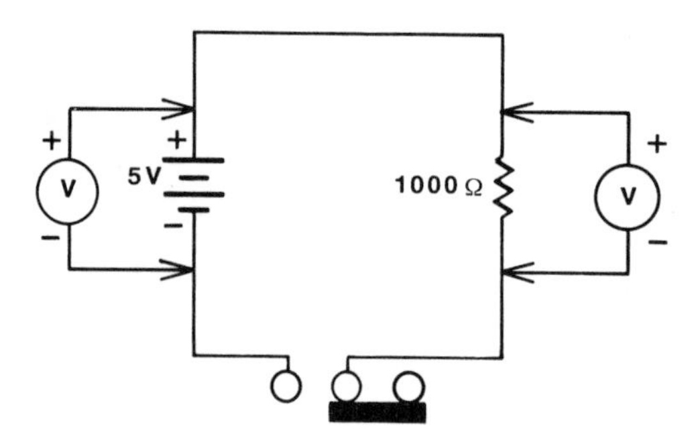

Figure E3-3
Schematic of a single-resistor series circuit.

4. Switch the Trainer on. Connect your voltmeter across the Trainer power supply leads and adjust the potential to +5 volts. This potential represents the voltage rise in the series circuit.

5. Now connect your voltmeter across the resistor leads in the 1-resistor series circuit. The voltage drop is ________V.

   No voltage is dropped because the current path is open at the switch.

6. Close the circuit switch. The voltage dropped across the resistor is now ________V. Does the voltage rise equal the voltage drop? ____________

7. Remove the voltmeter, open the circuit switch, and switch the Trainer off. Construct the circuit shown in Figure E3-4. Every place you see the symbol for an ammeter, put a short jumper wire in the circuit. Those jumpers will make it easier to insert an ammeter in various parts of the circuit in a later step.

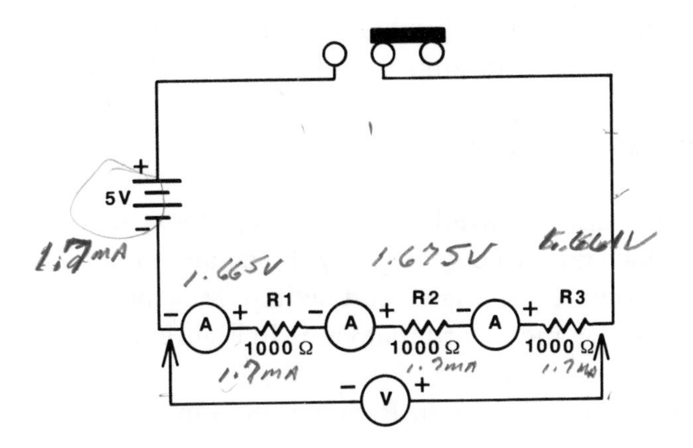

Figure E3-4
Schematic for a 3-resistor series circuit.

8. Measure the resistance of each resistor and record the values in Figure E3-5.

RESISTOR	OHMS	MEASURED CURRENT	CALCULATED VOLTS	MEASURED VOLTS
R1	1000Ω	1.7mA	1.66	1.76
R2	1000Ω	1.7mA	1.67	1.77
R3	1000Ω	1.7mA	1.66	1.76

4.99

Figure E3-5
Determining circuit characteristics.

9. Switch the Trainer on. The voltage rise is __5__ V.

10. Connect your voltmeter to the circuit as shown in Figure E3-4. Close the circuit switch. The voltage drop is __5__ V. Does the voltage drop equal the voltage rise? __yes__.

Again, the voltage rise equals the voltage drop. From the measurements you made in step 6 and in this step, you can conclude that the voltage rise always equals the voltage drop regardless of the resistance in the circuit.

11. Open the circuit switch. Remove the jumper connecting resistor R1 to the Trainer power supply. Place an ammeter in the circuit at that point. Close the circuit switch. Measure the current going to resistor R1 and record that value in Figure E3-5.

12. Open the circuit switch. Remove the ammeter and reinstall the jumper.

13. Following the procedure in steps 11 and 12, measure the current going to resistor R2 and resistor R3, and record those values in Figure E3-5. What can you conclude from these three measurements? ______________________________

____

You should have concluded that current is constant throughout a series circuit.

14. Using Ohm's Law, calculate the voltage drop across each resistor and record the values in Figure E3-5. The total voltage dropped by the three resistors is ______V. How does that compare with the voltage rise? ______________________________

____

15. Close the circuit switch and measure the voltage dropped by each resistor. Record the values in Figure E3-5. How does the calculated voltage compare to the measured voltage? __________

____

Discussion

You've accomplished several goals in this exercise. First, you observed that the source voltage, or voltage rise, always equals the total voltage dropped in a series circuit. Then you learned that the total voltage dropped is indeed equal to the sum of the individual voltages dropped in a series circuit. Finally, you determined that the current in a series circuit is constant throughout the circuit.

Having established the basic characteristics of a series circuit, you were able to calculate the voltage dropped by each component in the circuit, knowing its resistance and circuit current. Then you measured the voltage dropped by the components to verify your calculations. You could have just as easily calculated component resistance by measuring the voltage dropped by each component and circuit current.

Did you notice any differences between your calculated values and your measured values? Unless you used some very good equipment, you probable noted some degree of error. Recall that this error is basically caused by four factors. First, is the tolerance of the resistor values. Second is the accuracy with which you can "read" your instrument meters. Third, is the accuracy of your instrument measurement circuits. And fourth, is the "loading" effect of your instruments on the circuit. That is, how much does your test instrument change the operating characteristics of the circuit. For example, when you place an ammeter in the circuit, it will add a small amount of resistance to the circuit. That resistance will naturally decrease the amount of current flowing through the circuit. These and other test instrument characteristics will be described in detail in Unit 6.

The remainder of this exercise will give you an opportunity to modify the electrical characteristics of your series circuit and observe the results.

Procedure Continued

16. Open the circuit switch. Replace resistor R2 with a 100 Ω resistor. Make sure the voltage rise is still +5 volts.

17. The resistance of resistor R2 is ______Ω.

18. Close the circuit switch. Resistor R2 is dropping ______V.

19. Calculate circuit current. It is ______mA.

20. Resistor R1 is dropping ______V. Is this the same value you recorded in Figure E3-5? ______

21. Again calculate the circuit current, using the voltage drop you just measured and the resistance you recorded in Figure E3-5. It is ______mA. Does this match the calculated current in step 19? ______

22. Measure the circuit current. How does it compare to your calculated values? ______
Why is this current higher than the current recorded in Figure 3-5? ______

Discussion

Changing resistor R2 lowered circuit resistance by nearly 900 ohms. This, in turn, increased circuit current. With a higher current, the voltage dropped by resistor R1 was higher than the original measurement. The two calculated currents should have been approximately the same, taking into account any measurement errors. Similarly, the calculated and measured currents should have been about the same.

Procedure Continued

23. Open the circuit switch and switch the Trainer power off. Then remove the circuit parts.

24. Refer to Figure E3-6 and build the series circuit shown. If you are using a VOM, don't put the ammeter in the circuit until you adjust the Trainer power supply in the next step.

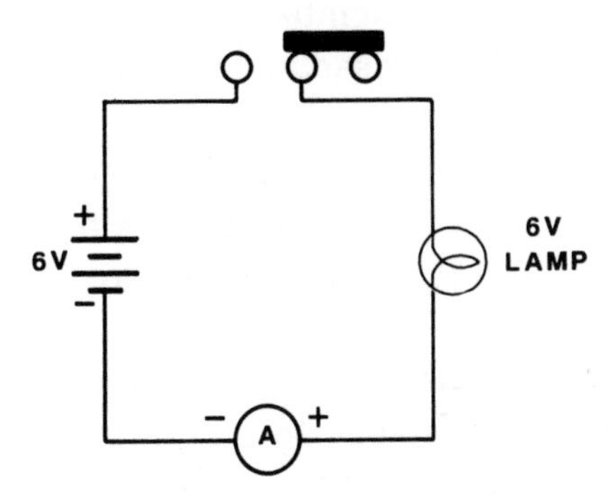

Figure E3-6
Schematic of a single-lamp series circuit.

25. Switch Trainer power on. Adjust the circuit voltage rise to 6 volts.

26. Close the circuit switch and measure circuit current. It is ________mA. Calculate the lamp resistance. It is ________Ω. Now, before you go to the next step, note the brightness of the lamp.

27. Open the circuit switch and add a second lamp in series with the first. Close the circuit switch and note the brightness of the two lamps. Why are they dimmer? ____________________
____

28. Now that you have doubled the number of lamps in the circuit, what do you expect the current to be? ________ mA Measure the circuit current. It is ________ mA. Is that what you expected? ________ Explain your answer. ____________________
____

29. Measure the voltage drop across the first lamp. Increase the Trainer power supply voltage until the voltage dropped across the first lamp is +6 volts. Using the lamp resistance calculated in step 26, calculate the circuit current. It is ________mA. Now measure the circuit current. Does it equal your calculated value? ________ Does it equal the current measured in step 26? ________ Explain your answer. ____________________
____

Discussion

The steps you performed in this section of the exercise are similar to those performed in the previous section. However, the results are not quite the same. If you remembered the tests you performed in Exercise 2, then you weren't surprised by the results.

When you added the second lamp in step 27, the lamps were dimmer than you noted in step 26. This was because the second lamp increased the resistance of the circuit, and as a result, lowered the current.

Since both lamps have essentially the same operating characteristics, you might expect the resistance to double and halve the current. But that wasn't the case. Recall that the amount of current passing through a lamp filament determines the amount of heat generated in the filament, and hence the resistance. Because there was less current, each bulb didn't get as hot as the single bulb did. Therefore, the resistance of each bulb in the 2-bulb circuit was less than the resistance of the bulb in the 1-bulb circuit. The resistance of the bulb in the 1-bulb circuit was approximately 122 ohms. Calculate the total resistance in the 2-bulb circuit and you will find it is approximately 180 ohms—each bulb has a resistance of about 90 ohms.

In step 29, you brought the circuit current up to the level that you originally established in step 26. The reason it was the same is because you reconstructed the same circuit characteristics. The voltage drop across the lamp in both steps was the same. The resistive characteristics of the lamp hadn't changed, so the current had to be the same. The only circuit characteristic that did change is the voltage rise. It's about twice the original voltage. That's because there are now two similar lamps in the circuit.

Procedure Continued

30. Open the circuit switch and switch the Trainer power off. Remove the parts from the Trainer and save them for future exercises.

31. This completes Exercise 3. Proceed to the next exercise, where you will study the electrical characteristics of parallel circuits.

EXERCISE 4

Parallel Circuits

PURPOSE: Show that voltage rise equals the voltage dropped in each branch of a parallel circuit.

Show that total current equals the sum of the branch currents in a parallel circuit.

Show that a change in resistance in one branch of a parallel circuit does not affect the resistance in any other branch.

Material Required

Trainer.
VOM or individual DC volt, ohm, and DC ammeters.

1 100 Ω resistor.
3 1000 Ω resistor.
2 6-volt lamp.
1 Slide Switch.
White #22 copper hook-up wire.

Introduction

In this exercise, you will have an opportunity to build several simple parallel circuits. As in the last exercise, you will be asked to measure the electrical characteristics of these circuits. You will also be asked to calculate different values from known or measured values.

Procedure

1. Make sure the Trainer is switched off, then construct the 1-lamp series circuit shown in Figure E4-1.

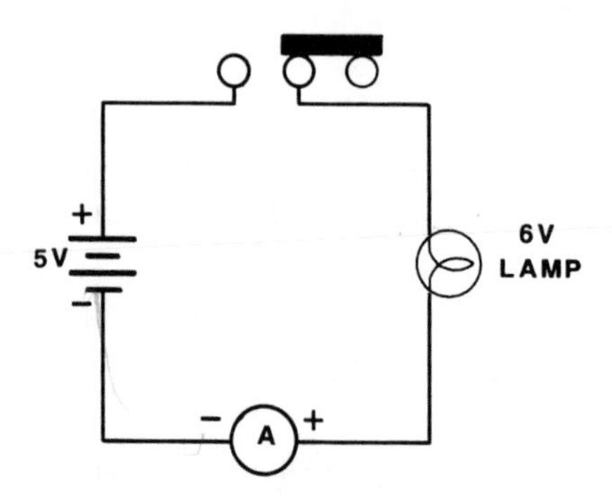

Figure E4-1
Schematic of a single-lamp series circuit.

2. Switch the Trainer on and adjust the power supply output for a voltage rise of +5 volts.

3. Close the circuit switch and measure the current. It is ________mA. Now measure the voltage drop across the lamp. It is ________V. Before you go to the next step, note the brightness of the lamp filament.

4. Open the circuit switch and add another lamp in parallel to the first. The circuit is shown in Figure E4-2. Close the circuit switch. Again look at the lamp filaments. Are they as bright? Why?

____

____

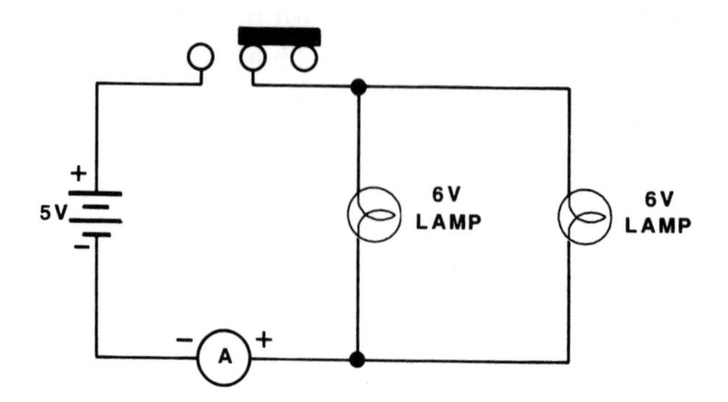

Figure E4-2
Schematic of a 2-lamp parallel circuit.

Recall that in a parallel circuit, the voltage dropped across each parallel branch equals the voltage rise. With the voltage drops equal, and the resistance of each lamp essentially equal, the current through each lamp is equal. Therefore, the filament in each lamp should be heated to the same brightness as in the 1-lamp series circuit. You'll verify this in the next step.

5. Measure the voltage drop across each parallel branch. It is ________V. That was pretty easy, since the lamp leads share the same connector blocks.

6. Now measure the current through each parallel branch. To do this, pull one one lead of a lamp, and then close the circuit with the ammeter. The first branch has a current of ________mA. The second branch has a current of ________mA.

   Any difference between the two branch currents is caused by a difference in lamp filament resistance. The current through the first branch should have matched the current you measured in step 3, since the voltage drop and lamp resistance haven't changed.

7. Knowing the individual branch currents, the total circuit current should be ________mA. It is ________mA. Were you right? If not, you should review Unit 2.

8. Knowing the individual branch currents and voltages, calculate the individual lamp resistances. The first lamp is ________Ω and the second lamp is ________Ω.

9. Knowing the individual branch resistances, the total circuit resistance should be ________Ω. Calculate the total resistance using the product-over-the-sum method. It is ________Ω. Were you right? Verify your answer by calculating the total resistance using Ohm's Law and total circuit current and voltage. It is ________Ω.

Discussion

These last nine steps have given you a chance to examine all of the electrical characteristics of a simple 2-resistor parallel circuit. You've verified that the voltage rise in a parallel circuit equals the voltage dropped by each parallel branch. You've also verified that total circuit current equals the sum of the individual branch currents. Finally, you've determined circuit resistance using two different methods— Ohm's Law and product-over-the-sum. The next part of the exercise will expand on what has been presented and give you a chance to calculate various circuit characteristics knowing other characteristics.

Procedure Continued

10. Measure the resistance of a 1000 Ω resistor. It is ________Ω.

11. Note the brightness of the lamps. Then open the circuit switch and add the 1000 Ω resistor in parallel with the two lamps. The circuit is shown in Figure E4-3.

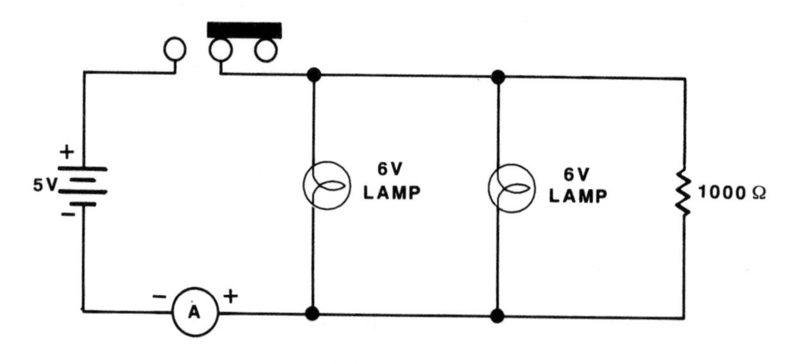

Figure E4-3
Adding a resistor to the 2-lamp parallel circuit.

12. Close the circuit switch. Did the lamps change in brightness? ________ Why? ____
____

The lamps didn't change brightness for the same reason they didn't change brightness when you went from a 1-lamp to a 2-lamp circuit in step 4. Adding another branch to a parallel circuit doesn't affect the operating characteristics of the other branches. It does, however, affect the operating characteristics of the circuit as a whole.

13. Using the circuit data recorded in the previous 12 steps, calculate the total circuit current. It is ________mA. Measure the current. It is ________mA.

Discussion

There are several methods for calculating total circuit current using the available data. Probably the easiest method is to first calculate the branch current. Simply divide the circuit voltage rise by the branch resistance recorded in step 10. Then add the calculated branch current to the other branch currents recorded in step 6. Any small error between the calculated and measured current is due to errors in your test equipment. Any large errors are due to a mistake in your calculations.

Procedure Continued

14. Open the circuit switch and replace the two lamps with two 1000 resistors. Close the circuit switch and measure the total circuit current. It is ________mA. Calculate total circuit resistance using Ohm's Law. It is ________Ω. Now calculate the resistance using the equal branch method. Assume each resistor has a value of 1000 Ω. This time total resistance is ________Ω. Are the results of your two calculations about the same, allowing for resistor tolerance? ________

Discussion

If there is a significant error, go back and measure the individual branch currents. Each one should be about 5 mA. Total circuit current should have measured about 15 milliamps. If any of the measured currents are wrong, you probably have a problem with meter linearity. That is, the meter has a built-in display error near the bottom or top end of each range. If that is the case, you will have to compensate by changing the range. While this may cause you to lose some resolution in your reading, you will, at least, be operating in the more linear area of your meter.

Procedure Continued

15. Open the circuit switch and replace the middle 1000 Ω resistor with the 100 Ω resistor. Now calculate the total circuit resistance assuming each resistor value is equal to its color code. It is ________Ω.

16. Close the circuit switch and measure total circuit current. It is ________mA. Use Ohm's Law to calculate total circuit resistance. It is ________Ω. Are the results of your two resistance calculations about the same, allowing for resistor tolerance? ________

Discussion

When you calculated total resistance in step 15, you didn't have three equal branch resistor values, thus you couldn't rely on the equal branch method to determine the resistance. The obvious solution is to use the product-over-the-sum method, first to combine two of the branches into one, and then to combine that value with the third branch. Another option is to use the equal branch method to combine the two 1000 Ω resistors—they equal 500 Ω. Then use the product-over-the-sum to combine the 500 Ω and 100 Ω branches. In either case, total resistance is approximately 83.33 Ω.

Knowing the circuit voltage drop and total circuit current, it's a simple matter to plug those values into Ohm's Law and calculate circuit resistance. How closely this resistance matches the resistance calculated in step 15 depends on the accuracy of your current measurement. By now, you should a fair idea how your ammeter responds. Therefore, the two resistance values should be pretty close.

Procedure Continued

17. Disconnect any test instruments, open the circuit switch, and switch the Trainer Power off. Remove the wire and parts from the Trainer and save them for future exercises.

18. This completes Exercise 4. Proceed to the next exercise, where you will study series-parallel circuits.

EXERCISE 5

Series-Parallel Circuits

PURPOSE: Demonstrate various types of series-parallel circuits.

Show how a change in circuit resistance in different parts of a series-parallel affects the entire circuit.

Material Required

Trainer.
VOM or individual DC volt, ohm, and DC ammeters.
1 270 Ω resistor.
1 470 Ω resistor.
3 1000 Ω resistor.
1 1000 Ω pot (to replace ET-3600 pot)*.
2 6-volt lamp.
1 Slide switch.
White #22 copper hook-up wire.

Introduction

Up to this point, you have studied series circuits and parallel circuits as individual types of circuits. In the real world, however, you seldom see them in their pure form. Rather, most circuits exist as combinations of series and parallel elements. In this exercise, you will have a chance to see how the characteristics of series and parallel circuits interact in a series-parallel circuit. You will build several series-parallel circuits, measure their electrical characteristics, and calculate many unknown values.

* If you are using a modified ET-3600 Analog Trainer to perform these exercises, there are a few circuits where the 1000 Ω pot on the Trainer may not provide enough range to allow the circuit to work. To ensure all of the circuits work, use the 1000 Ω pot supplied with the circuit parts whenever a step calls for the use of the 1000 Ω pot on the Trainer. This also applies to all of the remaining exercises.

Procedure

1. Make sure the Trainer is switched off, then construct the 2-lamp parallel circuit shown in Figure E5-1.

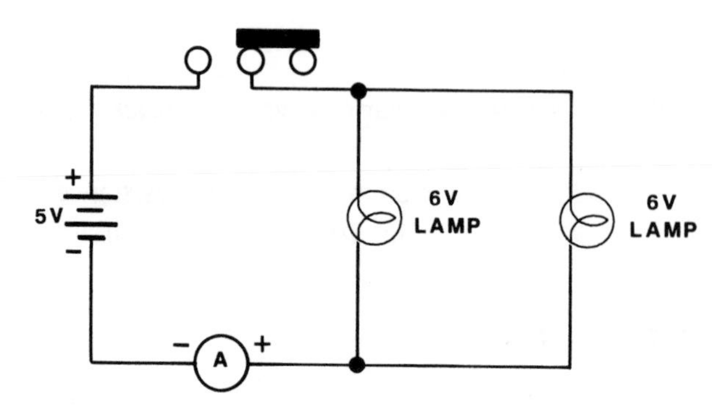

Figure E5-1
Schematic of a 2-lamp parallel circuit.

2. Switch the Trainer on and adjust the Trainer power supply output for a voltage rise of +5 volts.

3. Close the circuit switch and measure the current. It is ________mA. Note the brightness of the lamps.

4. Open the circuit switch. Refer to Figure E5-2 and place the 1000 Ω pot, located on the Trainer, in series with the ammeter in your original circuit. To make this connection, open the circuit between the ammeter and the lamps. Then connect the ammeter side of the circuit to the left, or bottom, (depending on Trainer model) connector block of the pot and the parallel branch side of the circuit to the center connector block of the pot.

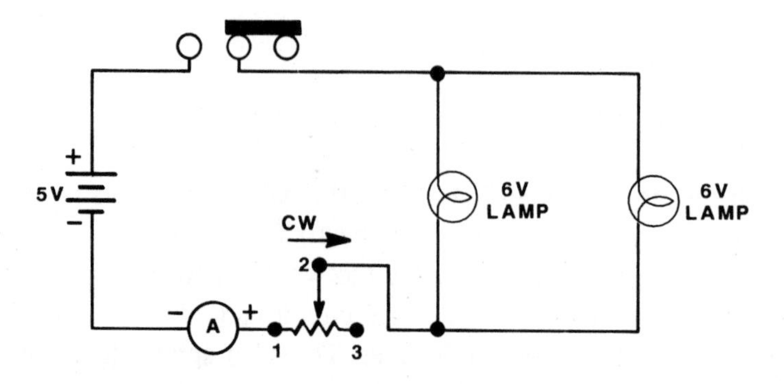

Figure E5-2
Schematic of the parallel circuit with a resistor in series with the source.

5. Rotate the pot wiper fully clockwise. You can see from the schematic, that this sets the pot for maximum resistance. Close the circuit switch. Did the lamps light? Why not? ________

____

6. Measure the circuit current. It is ______mA. Why is it so low?

____

____

7. Slowly rotate the pot wiper fully counterclockwise. As you do this, watch the lamps and your ammeter. What happened?

____

____

The ammeter now reads ________mA.

Discussion

Adding a large resistance in series with the power supply lowered total circuit current from about 80 mA to about 5 mA. That isn't enough current to light the lamps. Turning the pot wiper counterclockwise lowered the series resistance. Naturally, as the resistance went down, the circuit current increased. At about 40 mA, the lamps began to glow. The circuit you just built operates in a manner similar to the dashboard lighting circuit in a car.

Did the current you measured in step 3 equal the current you measured in step 7? That will depend on the pot. If the wiper goes all the way to the end of the resistive element, then the currents should match. If not, the current in step 7 is slightly lower. You determined the actual pot resistance in Exercise 1.

The first section of this exercise showed you that placing a resistance in series with the source voltage affects the total current of that circuit. What about placing a resistance in series with one of the branches? Are the other branches affected? What about the circuit as a whole? The next section will show you.

Procedure Continued

8. Open the circuit switch. Then move the pot from its current location in the circuit to a position in series with one of the branches, as shown in Figure E5-3. Be sure to close that portion of the circuit just opened by the removal of the pot.

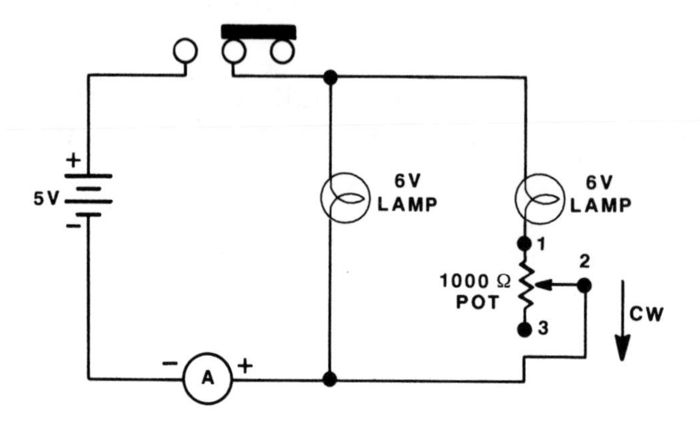

Figure E5-3

Schematic of the parallel circuit with a resistor in series with one of the branches.

9. Turn the pot wiper fully clockwise. Then close the circuit switch. Describe what you see. ____

____

What do you think is causing this effect? ______________________

____

10. Measure the current and voltage drop in each branch of the circuit. The branch with only a lamp has a current of ______mA and a voltage drop of ______V. The branch with the resistor in series with the lamp has a current of ______mA and a voltage drop of ______V.

11. Monitor the source current and the brightness of the two lamps as you slowly turn the pot wiper fully counter clockwise. What happened? ____

____

The source current is now ______mA.

12. Again measure the current and voltage drop in each branch of the circuit. The branch with only a lamp has a current of ______mA and a voltage drop of ______V. The branch with the resistor in series with the lamp has a current of ______mA and a voltage drop of ______V.

Discussion

When you first closed the switch in step 10, one lamp glowed, while the other didn't. The apparent cause for the lamp not glowing was the high resistance in that branch. This was verified when you measured the branch currents and voltage drops. Most of the circuit current was passing through the branch with only the lamp.

Turning the pot wiper counter clockwise reduced the branch resistance, and as a result, increased the branch current. When the current was high enough, the lamp began to glow. Increasing the branch current also increased the total circuit current.

When you again measured the branch currents and voltage drops, you found that the branch with only the lamp did not change. What did change was the current through the other branch and total circuit current. Thus, you can see that a change in the characteristics of a branch in a parallel circuit does not affect the characteristics of the other branch, only the circuit characteristics as a whole.

Now that you've had a chance to examine the characteristics of a simple series-parallel circuit, it's time to increase the complexity of the circuit and have you perform a few calculations.

Procedure Continued

13. Open the circuit switch, switch the Trainer power off, and remove all of the parts from the breadboarding area. Then build the circuit shown in Figure E5-4. Turn the wiper of the pot to about the center of its rotation.

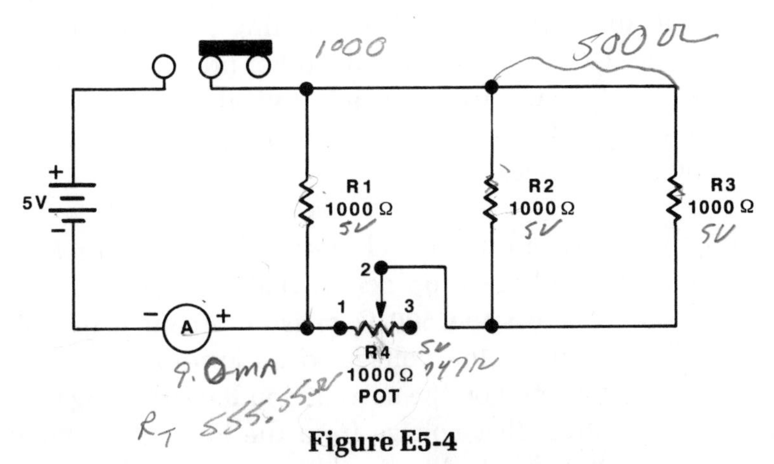

Figure E5-4

Complex circuit with an unknown resistance.

14. Switch the Trainer on and adjust the power supply for +5 volts. Close the circuit switch. Measure total circuit current. It is __5__ mA.

15. Knowing the voltage rise, total circuit current, and the value of the three fixed-value resistors, calculate the value of the pot. It is 555.55 Ω.

Discussion

To calculate the pot resistance in your circuit, you must apply the theories of both series and parallel circuits. The first step is to simplify the circuit as much as possible. Since you have two 1000 Ω resistors in parallel, they can be reduced, using the equal branch method, to an equivalent 500 Ω resistor that is in series with the pot. The simplified circuit is shown in Figure E5-5.

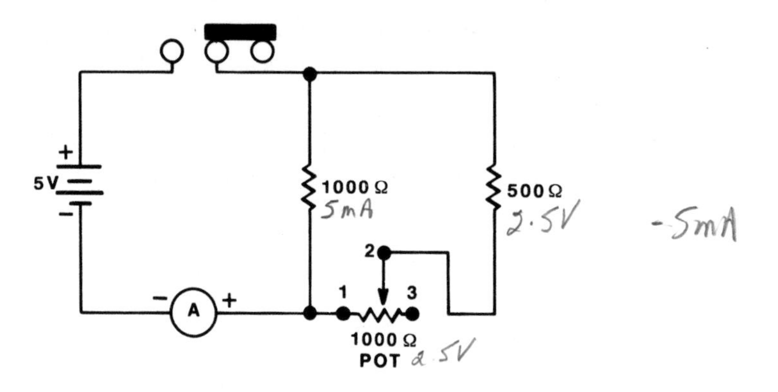

Figure E5-5
Complex circuit simplified.

The next step in the process is to determine how much current is passing through the parallel branch containing the unknown resistance. First calculate the current through the other branch. Using Ohm's Law, you know it is 5 mA. Subtract 5 mA from the current you measured in step 14 and you know the current flowing through the branch with the unknown resistance.

Knowing the current in the branch with the unknown resistance, you can calculate the voltage drop across that resistance. First calculate the voltage drop across the 500 Ω resistor. Again using Ohm's Law you should have found the voltage to be approximately 2.5 V. The actual value will depend on the current you have flowing through your circuit. Now subtract that voltage from the branch voltage drop, and you have the voltage dropped across the unknown resistance.

In the last step you use the calculated branch current, the calculated voltage drop, and Ohm's Law to calculate the resistance. Depending on how accurately you positioned the pot wiper, your answer should be approximately 500 Ω.

The last part of this exercise is provided to give you one more opportunity to hone your skills in observing and calculating the various characteristics of complex circuits.

Procedure Continued

16. Open the circuit switch and switch the Trainer power off. Remove the parts from the breadboarding area. Then construct the circuit shown in Figure E5-6.

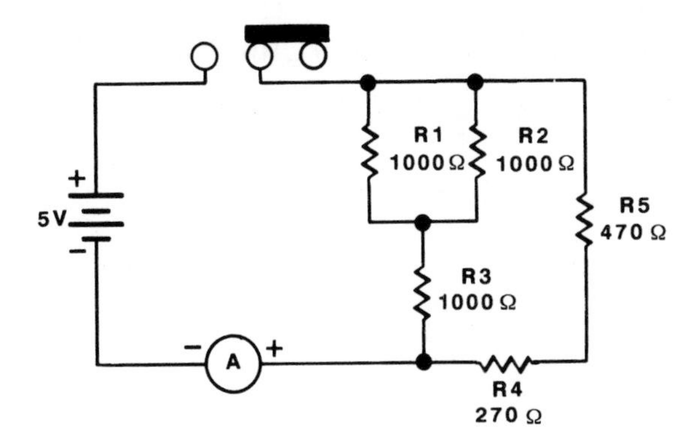

Figure E5-6
Schematic of a 5-resistor complex circuit.

17. Before you apply power to the circuit, calculate the total circuit resistance. It is ________Ω. If the circuit has a voltage rise of +5 V, the total circuit current should be ________mA.

18. Switch the Trainer on and set the power supply for +5 volts. Then close the circuit switch and measure total circuit current. It is ________mA. Is it what you expected? ________ If not, you may have miscalculated the resistance. Check your calculations.

19. Calculate the voltage drop across each resistor in the circuit, and record those values next to the resistors in the figure. Now verify your calculations by measuring the voltage drop across each resistor.

Discussion

If your measurements matched your calculations—within the limits of each resistor's tolerance and the accuracy of your instruments—you have met the goals of Unit 2. You know the basic characteristics of series, parallel, and complex circuits, and you know how to use Ohm's Law to determine an unknown electrical value.

Procedure Continued

20. This completes Exercise 5 and the exercises for Unit 2. Open the circuit switch and switch the Trainer power off. Remove the wire and parts from the Trainer, and save them for future exercises. Clean-up your work area.

21. Return to Unit 2 and complete the Unit Examination.

EXERCISE 6

Magnetism, Solenoids, And Relays

PURPOSE: Demonstrate the characteristics of a permanent magnet.

Demonstrate the characteristics of electromagnetism.

Demonstrate the construction and operation of a solenoid.

Demonstrate the construction and operation of a relay.

Material Required

Trainer.
Small soldering iron (25-35 watt).
Solder.
VOM or individual DC voltmeter and ohmmeter.
1 100 Ω, 2-watt resistor.
1 Slide switch.
1 Wire coil (inductor), Heath #45-601.
1 Relay, Heath #69-50.
1 Solenoid, Heath #69-121.
1 Compass, Heath #406-4.
1 Magnet, Heath #474-22.
White #22 copper hook-up wire.

Introduction

You've learned that magnetism plays a major role in the field of electricity. It provides a way to convert current flow into physical motion. In this exercise, you'll see how this concept works in a solenoid and in a relay. But first, let's examine the characteristics of magnetism, beginning with the permanent magnet.

Procedure

1. Position your compass on a flat surface, like a table-top. Make sure you don't put the compass near any metal objects like parts cabinets or steel supports. If the table-top is steel, place a couple of books between the compass and the table. Finally, make sure the compass needle swings freely on its pivot pin. Which end of the compass needle (painted or unpainted) points toward the geographic north pole of the Earth? PAINTED Which end of the needle (north or south) is painted? NORTH What is the magnetic polarity of the geographic north pole of the Earth? South

2. Set the magnet aside and remove the small magnet from its envelope—save the envelope. Position the magnet on a flat surface away from any metal objects. Now position the compass on the same flat surface, five or six inches from the magnet. Slowly slide the compass toward the magnet, until it is about one inch from the magnet. What did the compass needle do? N/Repel S,END Attach

3. Keeping the edge of the compass about one inch from the magnet, slide the compass around the magnet. What did the compass needle do? 1/2WAY AROUND needle face the same place magnet N end compass face South S END COMPASS NORTH

   What is the compass needle showing you? Attach of oppsite poles

4. The magnet has a small spot of paint at one end. What is the polarity of that end? NORTH

Discussion

The needle in your compass is actually a small magnet. The painted end of the needle is called the north pole because it points toward the geographic north pole of the Earth. Since the north pole of the compass is pointing toward the **geographic** north pole of the Earth, then that must also be the **magnetic** south pole of the Earth. That's because opposite poles of magnets attract each other.

The magnetic field surrounding the Earth is quite weak. Therefore, as you moved the compass toward the magnet, the needle stopped pointing north and south, and started reacting to the lines of flux surrounding the magnet. The closer you moved the magnet, the stronger the flux. As you moved the compass around the magnet, the needle followed the lines of flux. In fact, the needle is always oriented so the lines flow along the length of the needle. This concept is illustrated in Figure E6-1.

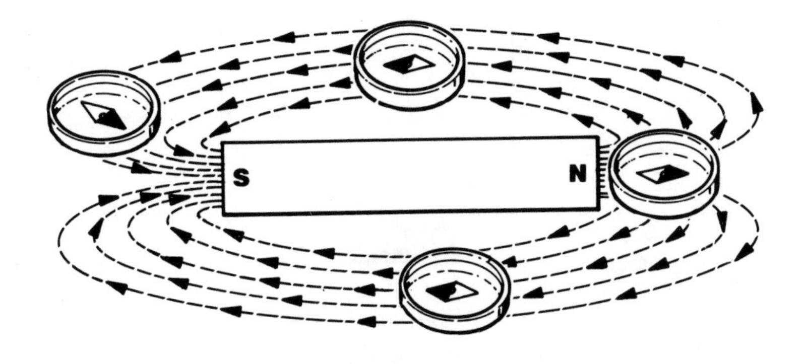

Figure E6-1

Tracing the magnetic lines of flux with a compass.

If you determined the correct polarity of the compass needle, then you should have been able to determine the correct polarity of the magnet. The north pole, painted end, of the compass always pointed toward the south pole of the magnet. Therefore, the painted end of the magnet is its north pole. By the way, if you to suspend the magnet by a thin cotton thread so it can swing freely, you will find the north end of the magnet always points toward the geographic north pole of the Earth, just like the compass.

Procedure Continued

5. Put the magnet back into its envelope and set it aside so you don't lose it.

6. If it hasn't already been done, take a 10-foot length of #22 copper hook-up wire and and remove a quarter-inch of insulation from each end. Then tightly coil the wire so there is a hole in the center of the coil about one inch in diameter. Use string or tape to secure the coiled wire--the tighter the wire bundle, the stronger the magnetic field. Now squeeze the sides of the coil so it is egg-shaped.

7. Refer to Figure E6-2 and build the circuit shown. Make sure the circuit slide switch is open, then switch the Trainer on and adjust the power supply for 10 V.

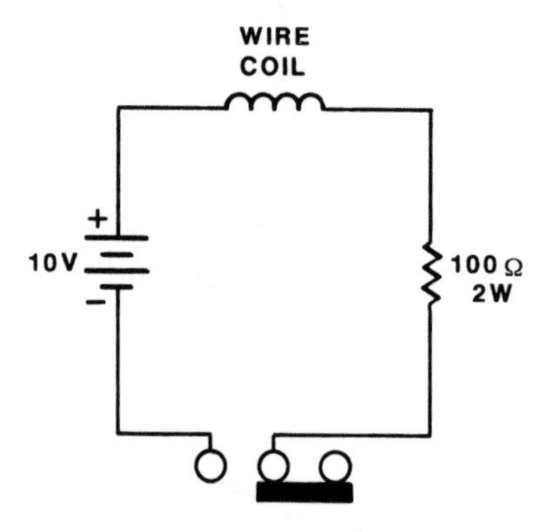

Figure E6-2
Circuit to demonstrate electromagnet characteristics.

NOTE: Shortly after you switch the circuit on, the current-limiting 2-watt resistor will get hot. It won't get hot enough to hurt you, but it will get your attention if you happen to touch it.

8. Position the coil of wire so it is standing straight up, with the two long-sides in the vertical position.

9. Examine the coil and locate the side where current will be flowing straight up when power is applied to the circuit. Using the left-hand magnetic-field rule, indicate in Figure E6-3 in which direction the compass needle will point when you switch power on and place the compass next to that side of the coil.

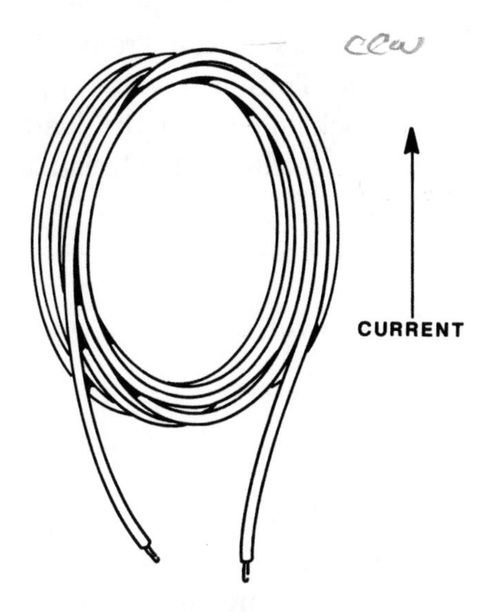

Figure E6-3
Coil of wire.

10. Switch the circuit on and verify your calculation. Move the compass completely around that leg of the coil. Notice that the needle always points in the direction of the lines of flux surrounding that side of the coil.

11. Switch the circuit off and replace your handmade coil of wire with the inductor. Don't bend the leads of the inductor too close to its body. You could stress the fine wire in the coil and break it.

NOTE: An inductor is simply a specially wound coil of wire that's used to control AC in some electrical circuits. In this exercise, you are using the inductor as an electromagnet.

12. Switch the circuit on and move the compass around the coil. How does the compass respond in comparison to the way it responded when you moved it around the permanent magnet? SAME THING ____________________

____

13. Note the direction the compass needle points when you hold it near the coil. Now switch the Trainer power off and reverse the circuit leads to the Trainer power supply. Switch the Trainer power on and recheck the magnetic characteristics of the coil with the compass. Have the characteristics changed? Yes
Why? Reversed ____________________

____

14. Switch the Trainer power off. Then remove the circuit components.

Discussion

You should have determined that when looking down on the coil, the lines of flux, on the side with the current flowing up, should rotate in a clockwise direction. That means the north end of the compass needle should also point in a clockwise direction.

You may have noticed that the compass needle didn't move smoothly as you rotated the compass around the vertical leg of the coil. That because the magnetic field of the coil is concentrated in the center of the coil, but very weak around the outside. Thus, when the compass is moved around the outside of the coil, the needle will track the movement. But when the compass gets near the center of the coil, the needle will turn abruptly, because of the intensified magnetic field.

When you moved the compass around the inductor, it should have reacted just like it did when you moved it around the permanent magnet. That's because the field around the coil is similar in intensity to that of the permanent magnet. Reversing the current flow through the coil reversed the polarity of the electromagnet, as verified by the compass.

The next part of this exercise shows you how the electromagnet is used to convert electrical energy into linear motion.

Procedure Continued

15. Locate the solenoid and its plunger. If it hasn't already been done, cut two 4-inch lengths of hook-up wire and remove a quarter-inch of insulation from each end of each wire. Solder a wire to each of the terminal lugs of the solenoid.

16. Switch the Trainer on and adjust the positive supply for 3 V.

17. Switch the Trainer off and connect the solenoid between the positive supply and ground. Remove the plunger from the solenoid.

18. Switch the Trainer on. Hold the solenoid in one hand, and slowly slide the plunger into the solenoid with the other hand. Take note of what happened.

19. Pull the plunger out of the solenoid. Increase the voltage to 6 V. Again, slide the plunger into the solenoid and note what happened.

20. Once again, pull the plunger out of the solenoid. Then increase the voltage to 12 V. Again, slide the plunger into the solenoid. Pull the plunger out of the solenoid. What did you learn in these last three steps? Volt determines amount of pull
more volts stronger pull

21. Switch the Trainer off. Disconnect the solenoid from the Trainer and pack it away with the plunger.

Discussion

The point of these steps is to let you see how a solenoid works. You should have noted two characteristics about the solenoid. First, the amount of voltage applied to the solenoid determines how much "pull" is generated by the electromagnet. Second, the further the plunger moves into the middle of the electromagnet, the greater the force exerted on the plunger. At 12 V, the electromagnet probably pulled the plunger out of your fingers, and then made it it very difficult for you to pull the plunger from the solenoid.

Procedure Continued

22. Locate the relay. With a small screwdriver, carefully pry the relay from its case, as shown in Figure E6-4A. Save the case.

23. Using a pencil, label the pins at the bottom of the relay, as shown in Figure E6-4B.

24. Examine the relay. Match the coil and switch terminals of the relay to those shown in Figure E6-4C. Write the five relay terminal numbers next to the five terminals shown in the schematic symbol in Figure E6- 4C.

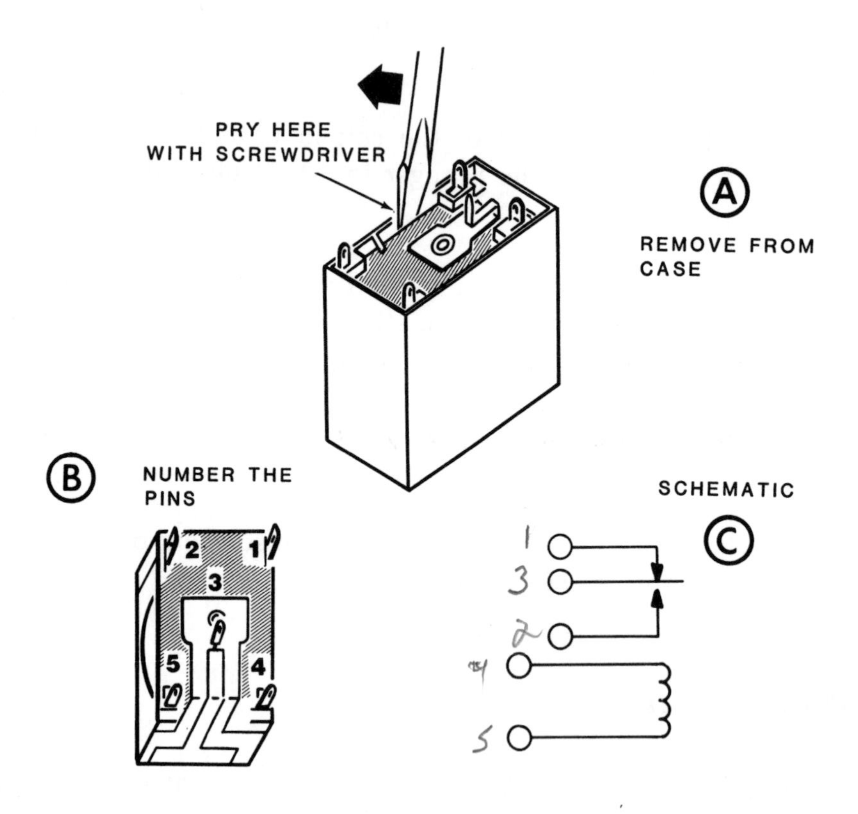

Figure E6-4

The relay.

25. If it hasn't already been done, cut two 3-inch lengths of hook-up wire. Remove a quarter-inch of insulation from each end of each wire. Then attach a wire to each relay coil terminal—wrap a wire end around a terminal and solder the connection.

26. Measure the resistance of the relay coil. It is .963 Ω.

27. Build the relay circuit shown in Figure E6-5. Adjust the power supply for minimum voltage.

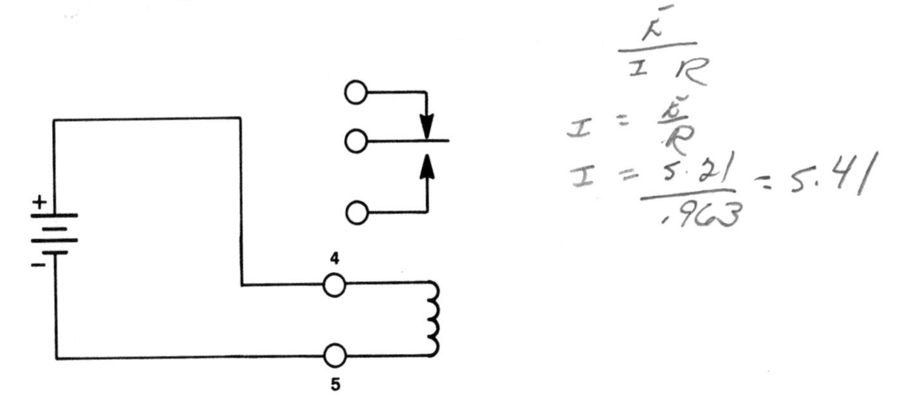

Figure E6-5
Relay circuit.

28. Switch Trainer power on. Slowly increase the voltage to the relay coil. Stop when the coil's magnetic field pulls the armature in (down). The the "pull-in" voltage is 5.21 V.

29. Using the voltage measured in step 28, and the resistance measured in step 26, calculate the current through the relay coil. The "pull-in" current is 5.41 mA.

30. Slowly decrease the voltage to the relay coil. Stop when the coil's magnetic field releases the armature. The "drop-out" voltage is 2.6 V.

31. Calculate the current through the relay coil. The "drop-out" current is 2.69 mA.

Why is there a difference between the pull-in current and the drop-out current? more volts to overcome spring force
____
____

32. Connect your ohmmeter to lugs 3 and 2 of the relay. The resistance is ___0___ Ω. Is this set of contacts normally open or normally closed? ___N/O___

33. Connect your ohmmeter to lugs 3 and 1 of the relay. The resistance is ___.2___ Ω. Is this set of contacts normally open or normally closed? ___N/C___

34. Slowly increase the voltage to the relay until it energizes. The resistance across lugs 3 and 1 is now ___0___ Ω.

35. Switch Trainer power off.

Discussion

Through observation and testing, you should have determined that the relay armature is connected to lug 3, lug 2 is normally open, and lug 1 is normally closed.

The pull-in current is approximately 6.3 mA and the drop-out current is approximately 3.7 mA. The basic reason why the pull-in current is greater that the drop-out current is the armature is further away from the coil in its de-energized state. Thus, it takes a larger magnetic field to pull the armature in against the spring pressure. Once the armature is pulled-in, the gap between the coil and the armature is much smaller, and thus a smaller magnetic field will hold the armature in place. If the current falls below the drop-out current level, the force of the armature spring exceeds the force of the magnetic field and the armature is pulled away from the coil.

Procedure Continued

36. Disconnect the relay from the Trainer and slide it back into its case. Save the relay and the other parts for future exercises.

37. This completes Exercise 6. Proceed to the next exercise, where you will study the operating characteristics of DC motors.

EXERCISE 7

DC Motors

PURPOSE: Demonstrate the operation of a permanent magnet DC motor.

Material Required

Trainer
Small soldering iron (25-35 watt).
Solder.
VOM or individual DC voltmeter.
Tape (masking or cellophane).
1 DC motor, Heath #420-644.
#22 copper hook-up wire—red, black, and white insulation colors.

Introduction

As you are aware, there is no basic type of DC motor. They come in all shapes, sizes, and configurations. To demonstrate each of these is just not practical. Therefore, this exercise will limit the description to a simple 3-pole, permanent magnet, DC motor, similar to those used in low-power, battery operated applications. Before we show you how the motor functions, let's examine its physical characteristics.

Figure E7-1 shows an end view of the inside of the motor. Like all typical DC motors, it contains field poles, an armature, commutator, and brushes. In this particular application, the brushes are stamped metal fingers, and the field poles are permanent magnets—nothing fancy. What is unique, however, is the armature. Instead of a two or four windings, like you studied in the unit, it uses three individual windings. These are tied together through a 3-segment commutator.

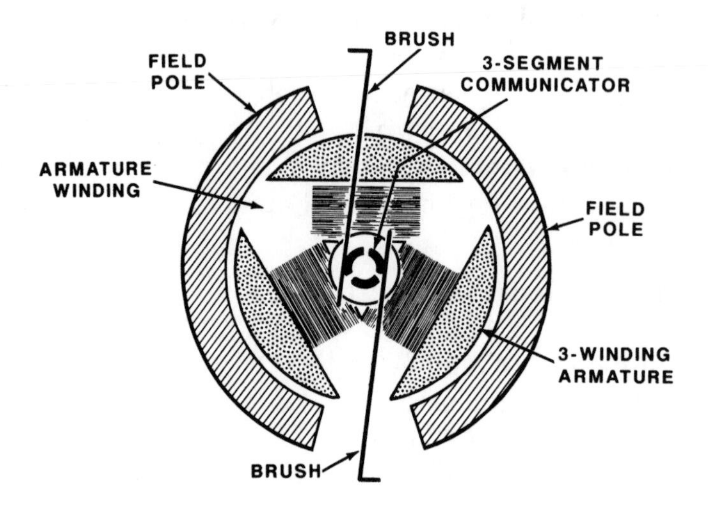

Figure E7-1
Internal construction of motor.

To see how a 3-winding armature is configured, look at Figure E7-2. On the right side of the figure is a schematic diagram of the armature. You can see that the windings are connected in series. The left side of the figure is a graphic representation of the armature. It shows that each winding connection is also tied to a commutator segment.

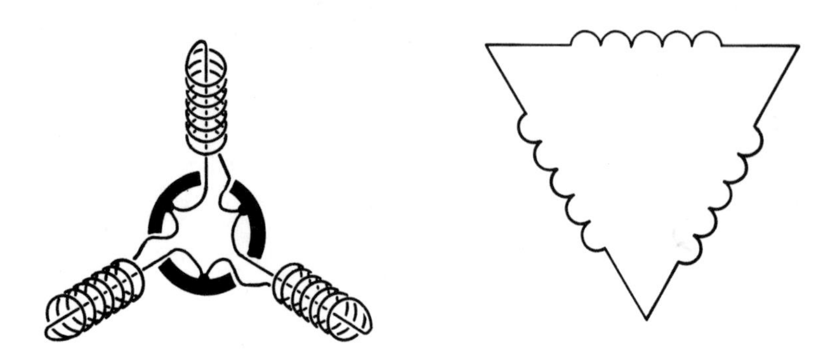

Figure E7-2
Graphic and schematic representation of a 3-winding armature.

Now compare Figure E7-1 with Figure E7-2. Can you see how the motor works? Figure E7-3 illustrates the process. The figure graphically shows the armature in three different points of rotation. As the armature turns, the brushes make contact with different parts of the commutator. This causes the current to flow through the windings in different directions with the rotation. Naturally, the polarity of the winding electromagnets changes with the change in current direction.

In Figure E7-3A, winding 1 is in series with the brushes, and windings 2 and 3 are in series with each other and the brushes. Current flow through winding 1 creates a north pole at its outer end—the winding is drawn toward the south field pole. At the same time, current flow through windings 2 and 3 create south poles at their outer ends—winding 2 is repelled by the south field and winding 3 is attracted to the north field pole.

In Figure E7-3B, current flow through windings 1 and 2 has not changed, thus their polarity has not changed. However, notice that the negative brush is touching the commutator segment on either side of winding 3. At this one point in its rotation, winding 3 is shorted out of the circuit—it is not an electromagnet.

Finally, in Figure E7-3C, the armature has rotated to the point where windings 1 and 3 are in series. Current flow creates north poles at the outer ends of windings 1 and 3. As a result, winding 1 is attracted to the south field pole and winding 3 is repelled by the north field pole. At the same time, current flow through winding 2 has not changed, and it is still attracted to the north field pole.

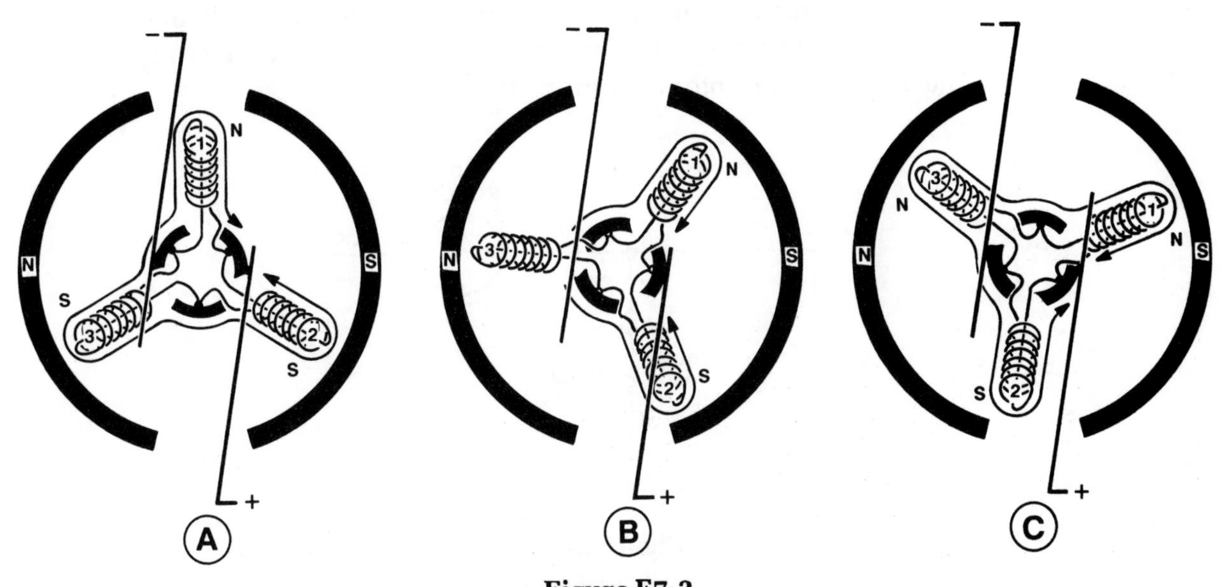

Figure E7-3

Current flow in the DC motor.

So, you can see that even though this particular DC motor has a different combination of armature windings and commutator segments, it still operates just like any DC motor. The advantage of this type of DC motor is that it can generate a lot of starting torque for its small size and cheap construction. Both of these characteristics are important in the small appliance and toy market where these motors are most often used. Now let's examine the operating characteristics of this motor.

Procedure

1. If the motor doesn't have wires attached to its terminals, prepare them in the following manner. Cut a 10-inch red wire and a 10-inch black wire from the wire supplied with the parts. Remove a quarter-inch of insulation from each end of each wire. Connect and solder the red wire to the motor terminal identified by the red spot. Then connect and solder the black wire to the other terminal.

2. Switch Trainer power on and adjust the positive DC supply for 6 V. Then switch Trainer power off.

3. Refer to Figure E7-4 and build the circuit shown. Use the 1000 Ω pot on the Trainer for the variable resistor. Be sure to use the correct terminals of the pot—the red motor wire and the wire from the positive side of the power supply go to terminal 1. Next, connect your voltmeter across the leads of the motor, so you can monitor the voltage dropped by the motor. Then, turn the knob on the pot fully counterclockwise. Finally, stick a small piece of tape on the shaft of the motor. This will help you determine the direction the motor is turning, in a later step.

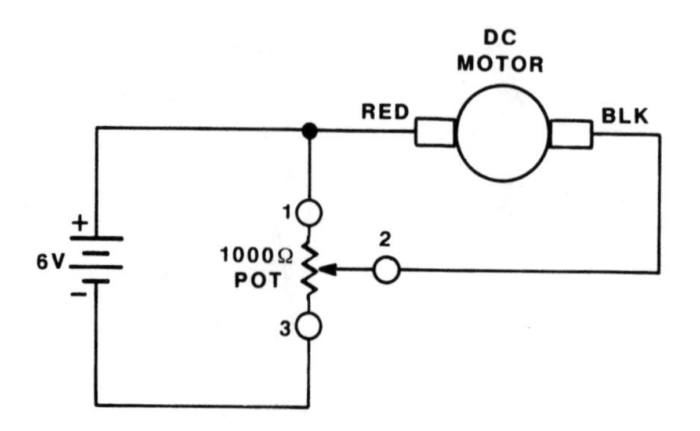

Figure E7-4

Motor test circuit.

4. Switch Trainer power on—the motor should not run at this time. Switch the Trainer power off. Why didn't the motor run?
____
____
____

5. Switch Trainer power on and slowly rotate the pot knob clockwise until the motor begins to run. Note the speed of the motor and the amount of voltage dropped by the motor. Now slowly rotate the pot knob counterclockwise until the motor stops running. Again, note the voltage. Switch Trainer power off. Why did it take more voltage to start the motor running than it did to keep the motor running? ____________________
____
____

6. Switch Trainer power on and slowly rotate the pot knob back and forth, through its complete range of travel. Note the operation of the motor. Then switch Trainer power off. What effect does changing the position of the pot wiper have on the motor?
____
____

Why does the motor react in this fashion? __________
____
____

7. Switch Trainer power on and adjust the pot so the motor is running slowly. Look at the end of the motor with the shaft. In what direction is the armature turning? __________ If you were to reverse the current through the motor, would it continue to rotate in the same direction? __________

8. Switch Trainer power off. Reverse the connections of the motor leads at the pot. Switch Trainer power on and adjust the pot so the motor is running slowly. In what direction is the armature turning? __________ Switch Trainer power off and explain why the motor ran the way it did. ____________________
____

Discussion

The motor didn't run, the first time you applied power to the circuit, because almost all of the voltage was dropped across the pot. As you turned the pot knob clockwise, you increased the voltage to the motor. The motor started running at about 1.5 V, yet it continued to run down to about 0.4 V. That's because it takes more magnetic force to overcome bearing friction and to provide the initial push to start rotation. Once the armature is spinning, its weight (mass) acts like a flywheel to keep the armature spinning. Thus, the motor continues to run at a lower voltage.

Changing the position of the pot wiper changed the amount of voltage dropped across the pot and the motor. As the motor voltage increased, the current through the motor increased. That, in turn, increased the current through the windings, and hence the magnetic force generated by the windings. The higher the voltage, the greater the force, and the faster the armature spins. Decrease the voltage and the force decreases—the armature spins slower.

If the red terminal of the motor is connected to the positive side of the power supply, the armature will spin in a clockwise direction. Reverse the motor leads, and the armature will spin in a counterclockwise direction. The rotation is reversed because the current flow through the motor is reversed. That, in turn, reverses the magnetic field generated in the windings.

Procedure Continued

9. This completes Exercise 7 and the exercises for Unit 3. Remove the tape from the shaft of the motor. Then remove the wire and motor from the Trainer, and save them for future exercises. Clean-up you work area.

10. Return to Unit 3 and complete the Unit Examination.

EXERCISE 8

AC Characteristics

PURPOSE: Demonstrate the various AC waveforms produced by the Trainer.

Compare the AC measuring methods peak-to-peak, peak, and effective, or rms.

Demonstrate the AC characteristics of your test equipment.

Material Required

Trainer.
VOM or individual AC voltmeter.
Oscilloscope (dual-channel recommended).
White #22 copper hook-up wire.

Introduction

Up to this point, you have only experimented with DC. You have studied its characteristics, constructed series, parallel, and complex circuits powered by DC, and used Ohm's Law to determine various electrical unknowns. In this and the following exercise, you will concentrate on AC.

As you proceed through these exercises, you will find that in terms of Ohm's Law, AC isn't any different from DC. However, because it is an alternating current, it doesn't always display the same characteristics as DC when it is used with certain electrical devices. Many of those differences are illustrated in the exercises.

Working with AC, you will find that an oscilloscope is a very valuable tool. It's valuable because it shows you exactly what the AC waveform looks like, the frequency of each cycle, and the peak and peak-to-peak voltage levels. Meters, on the other hand, are limited to measuring effective, or rms, levels of voltage or current. Unless you know what the waveform looks like, you can never be sure of what you are measuring. You'll get a chance to see how this can happen.

You will be working with an oscilloscope in this exercise. However, because of the general complexity of the instrument and the many different designs on the market, we must rely on your instructor to explain the operation of the oscilloscope you will be using.

Whenever you are asked to measure or calculate the value of an electrical quantity, always attach the appropriate units (A, V, Ω) to the number you write down. In addition, for values of AC current or voltage, you should indicate the method of measurement used (peak, peak-to-peak, or rms).

Procedure

1. Switch your Trainer and oscilloscope on. Adjust your oscilloscope controls as follows:

   Channel 1 and Channel 2 vertical position controls—centered.
   Channel 1 and Channel 2 AC/GND/DC input select switches—GND.
   Channel 1 and Channel 2 VOLTS/CM vertical deflection range switches—20 V (2 V if × 10 oscilloscope probe used).
   TIME/CM (time base) switch—5 ms.
   TRIG SELECT switch—LINE.
   TRIG MODE/COUPLING—AUTO or AC.
   INTENSITY—optimum.
   FOCUS—optimum.
   Horizontal position control—set to start trace at left edge of display grid.
   All of the variable input attenuation and time base controls to their calibrated position.

   We assume you are using a dual-channel oscilloscope. If you only have a single-channel oscilloscope, there will be a couple of signal comparisons that you cannot perform.

   Remember, to obtain accurate amplitude measurements, you must allow for any attenuation through your scope probe. Most probes reduce the signal by a factor of 10 (× 10 attenuation), or they do not reduce the signal at all (× 1 attenuation).

2. Using the Channel 1 and Channel 2 vertical position controls, center both traces in your oscilloscope display. This is the zero voltage, or ground, reference line for your display.

3. Use short pieces of hook-up wire to connect the Channel 1 probe between one of the 15 VAC connector blocks and the center ground connector block. Be sure the probe ground wire is connected to the ground connector block.

4. Set the Channel 1 AC/GND/DC switch to AC. If necessary, adjust the TRIG LEVEL control for a stationary display. You should see a sine wave pattern on your display approximately 2 centimeters high. The peaks of the sine wave will be flattened a small amount. But don't worry, this is typical of the output. Notice where the trace is located on the display. It is centered over the reference ground line. Half of the waveform is a positive voltage and half of the waveform is a negative voltage. This verifies what you learned about alternating current. First, the current moves in one direction, and then it moves in the other, building and falling with every half-cycle. At the point where the trace crosses the reference ground line, the current is switching direction, and thus there is no current flow.

5. Reposition the trace so it is above the center of the display. Again, if necessary, adjust the TRIG LEVEL control for a stationary display. Set the Channel 1 AC/GND/DC switch to GND. Where is the reference ground line for Channel 1 now? It moved when you repositioned the trace. Thus, the trace is still centered over the reference ground line for Channel 1. Set the Channel 1 AC/GND/DC switch back to AC.

6. Again use short pieces of hook-up wire to connect the Channel 2 probe between the other 15 VAC connector block and the center ground connector block. Be sure the probe ground wire is connected to the ground connector block. Otherwise, you will short out the AC signal.

7. Set the Channel 2 AC/GND/DC switch to AC. You should see a second clipped sine wave pattern on your display just like the the one in Channel 1. Note that it is centered over the reference ground line established for Channel 2. Reposition the trace so it is below the center of the display.

8. Draw a representation of your oscilloscope display in the space provided in Figure E8-1. The Channel 1 input voltage is 15VAC. The Channel 2 input voltage is 15VAC.

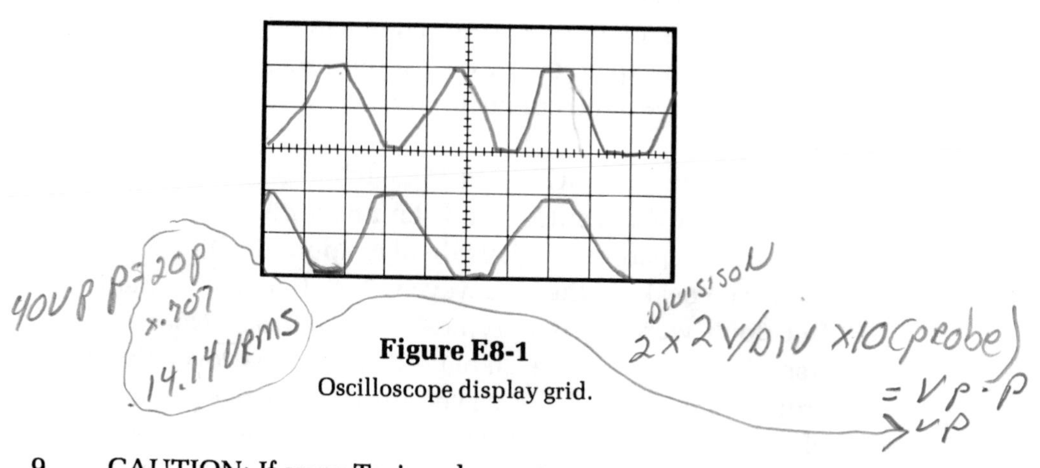

Figure E8-1
Oscilloscope display grid.

9. CAUTION: If your Trainer has a 3-prong power plug, **do not** perform this step, you could short-out the transformer in the Trainer power supply. Refer to Page 6, note 2, for further information. Disconnect your Channel 2 probe from the Trainer. Then reconnect your Channel 1 probe to the 30 VAC connector blocks. Reposition the trace so it is centered in the display. The signal voltage is ________.

10. Disconnect your Channel 1 probe from the Trainer. Then measure the 30 VAC output with your AC voltmeter. It is 30.06VAC.

11. Measure each of the 15 VAC outputs. One is 15VAC and the other is 15.06VAC.

12. Compare your oscilloscope and voltmeter readings. What can you conclude from these readings? ____

Discussion

In this part of the exercise, you examined the "line frequency" 15 and 30 VAC Trainer outputs. The outputs are produced by "tapping" a portion of the Trainer power supply current through a transformer secondary winding. Figure E8-2 is a schematic diagram of the transformer section of the ET-3100B Trainer power supply. It shows how one of the secondary windings of the transformer is used to supply the 30 VAC output. The two 15 VAC outputs are produced by referencing the center of the transformer winding to ground.

Notice that in this particular Trainer, reference ground is also connected to earth ground through the ground prong of the line cord plug. All of Heath Company's Analog Trainers, that have 3-wire line cords, connect circuit ground to earth ground. You can see that if you connect a scope probe to the two 30 VAC connectors, you will short-out half of the transformer winding. That's because the scope ground lead is tied to earth ground. As a result, the center tap of the transformer and one end of the transformer are tied to the same point—earth ground. Different ground symbols are used to represent earth and circuit ground in the schematic.

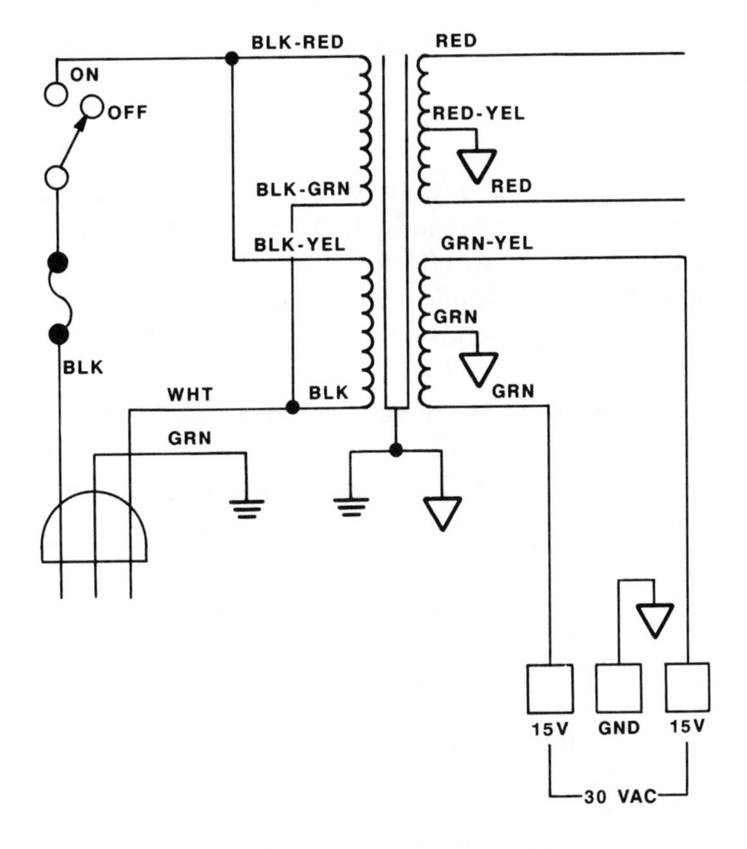

Figure E8-2
ET-3100B power supply transformer circuit.

You may have wondered why the sine wave patterns you drew in Figure E8-1 had flat tops. It is caused by a power supply loading effect that is reflected back into the transformer windings. A better explanation of this characteristic is, as you might imagine, beyond the level of this course's presentation.

If you used a dual-channel oscilloscope, you should have noticed that the waveforms you drew in Figure E8-1 were not exactly identical. Rather, they were mirror images of themselves. This occurred because both voltages were referenced to ground at the middle of the transformer winding. Thus, as one voltage was increasing, with respect to ground, the other was decreasing.

Speaking of voltage, did you understand why the voltage you measured with your oscilloscope was very different from the voltage you measured with your voltmeter? The voltage you observed on the oscilloscope was peak-to-peak voltage. You should have recorded a value of approximately 43 V peak-to-peak for both of the 15 VAC outputs, and approximately 86 V peak-to-peak for the 30 VAC output. Naturally, the actual values depend on the output characteristics of the Trainer's secondary transformer winding.

When you measured the outputs with your voltmeter, you probably recorded levels of approximately 15 VAC and 30 VAC. This is what you would expect from an effective, or rms, reading meter, since the Trainer outputs are specified in rms voltage. Again, the actual values depend on the transformer output.

You can verify that these voltages are rms values with a couple of simple calculations. For example, assume the voltage at the 15 VAC output is 43 V peak-to-peak. Then the first step is to convert the peak-to-peak voltage to a peak voltage using the formula:

$$\text{PEAK VOLTAGE} = \frac{\text{PEAK-TO-PEAK VOLTAGE}}{2}$$

$$\text{PEAK VOLTAGE} = \frac{43\text{ V}}{2}$$

$$\text{PEAK VOLTAGE} = 21.5\text{ V}$$

Next, convert the peak voltage to effective, or rms, voltage with the formula:

RMS VOLTAGE = PEAK VOLTAGE × 0.707

RMS VOLTAGE = 21.5 V × 0.707

RMS VOLTAGE = 15.2 V

Thus, you can see that 43 V peak-to-peak is equal to 15.2 V rms.

Now that you know how to use the oscilloscope to measure voltage, it's time to learn how to determine the frequency of an AC waveform displayed on an oscilloscope. This is described in the next section of the exercise.

Procedure Continued

13. Make sure the trace on your oscilloscope is vertically centered in the display. Then count the number of horizontal squares that one cycle of the sine wave covers. Try to be as accurate as possible. It is 3.5 squares.

14. Now calculate the frequency of the sine wave using the formula F = 1 / T. In this formula, F is frequency in Hertz and T is the time it takes to complete one cycle, in seconds. Since your oscilloscope horizontal display time base is set for 5 ms (5 milliseconds), each square on your display grid is equal to 0.005 s (0.005 seconds). The frequency of the sine wave displayed on your oscilloscope is 57.14.

$F = \frac{1}{.005 \times 3.5}$

$F = \frac{1}{.0175}$

F = 57.14 Hz

Discussion

Not only does the oscilloscope show you what an AC waveform looks like, it also gives you enough information to calculate the frequency of the waveform. Since you were observing a sine wave generated by the power supply transformer, you should have calculated a frequency of 60 Hz plus or minus a few tenths of a Hertz. For example, assume one cycle of the sine wave covered 3.3 grid squares. Then using the formula for time:

$$T = \text{Time Base} \times \text{Grid Count}$$

$$T = 0.005\ \text{s} \times 3.3$$

$$T = 0.0165\ \text{s}$$

It takes 0.0165 seconds to complete one cycle of the trace. Knowing time, you can calculate frequency using the formula:

$$F = \frac{1}{T}$$

$$F = \frac{1}{0.0165\ \text{s}}$$

$$F = 60.61\ \text{Hz}$$

Identifying a display grid division of less than a tenth is very difficult. For that reason, you can't precisely determine the frequency of a waveform using the oscilloscope. However, as you can see, you can get close to the actual value. One thing you can be sure of, the 60 Hz current generated by the power company is quite reliable. They normally operate within a frequency deviation of less than ±0.004 Hz. The actual error, at any point in time, depends on the electrical load on their power lines.

In the following steps, you will examine the other AC outputs on the Trainer.

.002 x 8.5 = .017 = 58.8

Procedure Continued

15. Connect Channel 1 of your oscilloscope to the Sine wave connector block in the Generator section of your Trainer and a GND connector block. Adjust the Trainer Generator frequency for approximately 1000 Hz.

    Now, to get a display that is usable, readjust the Channel 1 VOLTS/CM range switch to produce a display that is between 2 and 5 divisions high. Change the TRIG SELECT switch to Channel 1. Set the TIME/CM switch to display at least two complete cycles of the sine wave.

    What you see is a sine wave signal that is generated by an oscillator circuit in the Trainer. The peak-to-peak voltage is 1.59V.

16. Now connect the square wave output from the Generator section of your Trainer to Channel 2 of your oscilloscope. Its peak-to-peak voltage is 11.6.

17. Depending on the Trainer, one of the waveforms is larger than the other. To make the following tests, you need to reduce the voltage level of the larger waveform. To do this, first position the wiper of the 100 kΩ pot, on the Trainer, to the center of its rotation. Then connect the Trainer output with the larger waveform, and its associated oscilloscope input, to the 100 kΩ pot. Figure E8-3 shows how the square wave output and the channel 2 input probe would be connected.

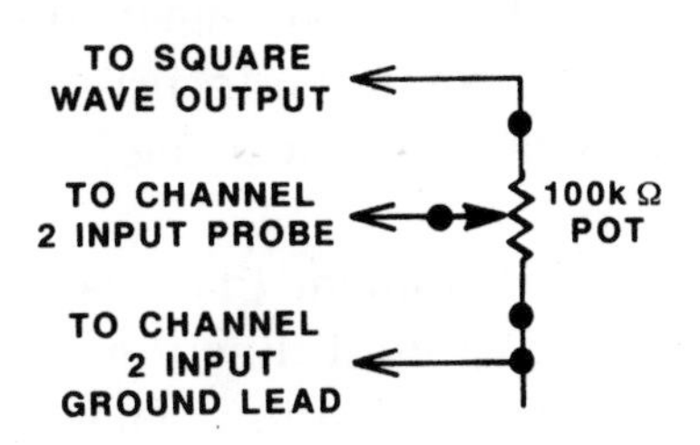

Figure E8-3

Circuit to control the voltage level of the Trainer square wave.

18. Set the Channel 2 VOLTS/CM switch to the same range as the Channel 1 VOLTS/CM switch. Center the two traces in the display. Then adjust the 100 kΩ pot to reduce the larger waveform trace to the same amplitude (peak-to-peak voltage) as the smaller waveform trace. You now have two different AC waveforms with the same peak-to-peak voltages. Do you think your AC voltmeter will agree that the voltages are the same?

19. Measure the voltage of the two AC outputs at the connector blocks where you have your oscilloscope probes connected. The rms sine wave voltage is 4.18, and the rms square wave voltage is 6.44. Why are the two rms voltages different? ______

______

Discussion

You've examined two different AC waveforms and discovered that while they have the same peak-to-peak voltages, they do not have the same rms voltages. Recall from Unit 3 that a meter that measures rms voltage is only accurate when it is measuring a sine wave. It's a function of how the meter circuits respond to alternating current.

In this particular example, the difference in rms voltage between a sine wave and a square wave of equal amplitude is large. When you measure an AC voltage that has a waveform that is closer in shape to a sine wave, the difference is smaller. However, there will be a difference. If you have an ET-1000 Trainer, you can measure the Generator section's Triangle wave output and see what we mean. The point we are trying to make, is know what you are measuring before you make any assumptions that may lead you to an incorrect conclusion. If possible, examine the waveform with an oscilloscope.

There is another common problem that may cause you to make an incorrect measurement. Most multifunction meters do not respond to high frequency AC in a linear fashion. That is, a 1-volt rms reading at a frequency of 60 Hz may decrease to less than 1-volt rms at 6000 Hz. This is illustrated in the following steps.

Procedure Continued

20. If the Trainer's square wave output and the Channel 2 scope probe are connected to the 100 kΩ pot, disconnect them. Connect the sine wave output and the Channel 1 probe to the 100 kΩ pot, as described in step 17. Then, connect your AC voltmeter to the same connector blocks as the oscilloscope probe, that is, the pot wiper and ground.

21. Vary the frequency of the sine wave from its slowest rate, to its fastest rate, and observe the amplitude of the waveform. You will see the amplitude change, to some degree, with the change in frequency. Since you don't want that change in frequency to affect your measurements in the following steps, you will use the 100 kΩ pot to maintain a constant amplitude.

22. Set the sine wave output frequency to approximately 1000 Hz. Adjust the 100 kΩ pot for an output of about 0.5 volts rms. Then set the oscilloscope Channel 2 input range to 50 mV/CM. Readjust the pot for a 150 mV peak-to-peak (3 CM) sine wave display. The voltmeter reads ________.

23. Adjust the sine wave output to its greatest frequency. Depending on your Trainer, this is approximately 20 kHz or 100 kHz. Readjust the 100 kΩ pot for a 150 mV peak-to-peak display. The voltmeter now reads ________.

Discussion

Unless you are using an AC voltmeter that is designed to measure high frequency AC voltages, you should have noted a significant difference in voltage between steps 22 and 23. Because you made sure the peak-to-peak voltage was the same between steps, the error must lie within the meter. As you will learn in Unit 6, common multifunction meters do not respond well to high frequency voltage and current. Keep this in mind when you work with these meters. If you aren't sure about a particular voltage reading, check the response of your meter with a known voltage at a known frequency. Better yet, use an oscilloscope and mathematically convert the peak-to-peak display to an rms voltage.

Procedure Continued

24. Switch the Trainer off. Disconnect the oscilloscope and meter, and remove the wires from the Trainer. Save them for future exercises.

25. This completes Exercise 8. Proceed to the next exercise, where you will study the relationship between alternating current and Ohm's Law.

EXERCISE 9

Ohm's Law And AC

PURPOSE: Demonstrate the fact that Ohm's Law applies to alternating current in the same way that it applies to direct current.

Provide an opportunity to calculate current, voltage, and resistance in series, parallel, and series-parallel circuits operating with AC.

Show how power is calculated using the rms values of AC current and voltage.

Material Required

NOTE: Parts of this, and later, exercises require an AC milliammeter. This is not a common instrument. If one is not available, you will have to skip those steps that require you to measure AC current, or you will have to measure the resistance and voltage, and then use Ohm's Law to calculate the current.

Trainer.
VOM or individual AC and DC volt, ohm, and AC and DC ammeters.
Oscilloscope.
1 270 Ω resistor.
2 470 Ω resistor.
2 1000 Ω resistor.
2 6-volt lamp
1 Slide switch.
White #22 copper hook-up wire.

Introduction

Now that you are familiar with some of the physical characteristics of AC and its measurement standards, it's time to see how AC relates to Ohm's Law. In this exercise, you will construct several different types of circuits and measure their electrical characteristics. In many instances, we will ask you to use Ohm's Law to calculate an unknown value.

Whenever you are asked to measure or calculate the value of an electrical quantity, always attach the appropriate units (A, V, Ω) to the number you write down. In addition, for values of AC current or voltage, you should indicate the method of measurement used (peak, peak-to-peak, or rms).

Let's begin the exercise by looking at AC within the series circuit.

Procedure

1. Switch your oscilloscope and any powered meters on.

2. Refer to Figure E9-1 and construct the simple series circuit shown. Use the SINE wave output from the Function Generator on your Trainer as the circuit power supply. Notice that the meters shown in the figure are polarized even though they are AC meters. This is done to remind you that if you are using a meter that has an AC power supply, one lead of the meter is referenced to ground. Remember, you MUST connect that lead to the ground connector of the Trainer.

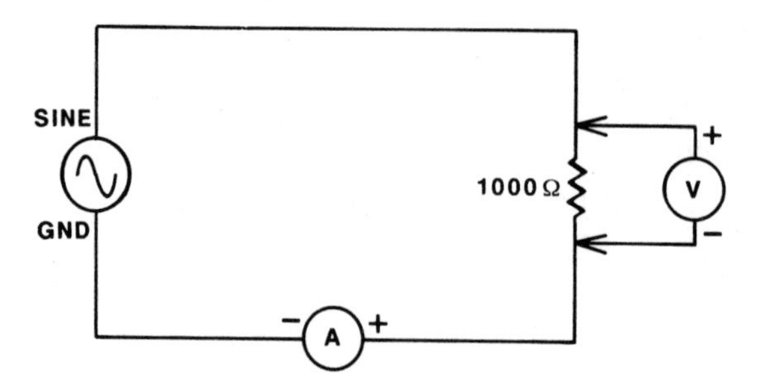

Figure E9-1
Schematic diagram of the test circuit using a fixed resistor.

3. Switch your Trainer power on and adjust the generator frequency for about 1000 Hz. Measure the current flowing through the circuit. The current is ________. Use Ohm's Law to calculate the voltage drop. The calculated voltage drop is ________.

4. Measure the voltage drop. (If you are using a VOM, remember to switch the meter to the AC volts scale **before** connecting it across the source.) The measured voltage drop is ________. Are the calculated and measured values equal? ________

5. Switch Trainer power off and wire the 1000 Ω Trainer pot in series with the 1000 Ω circuit resistor, as shown in Figure E9-2. Rotate the pot wiper near the center of its rotation.

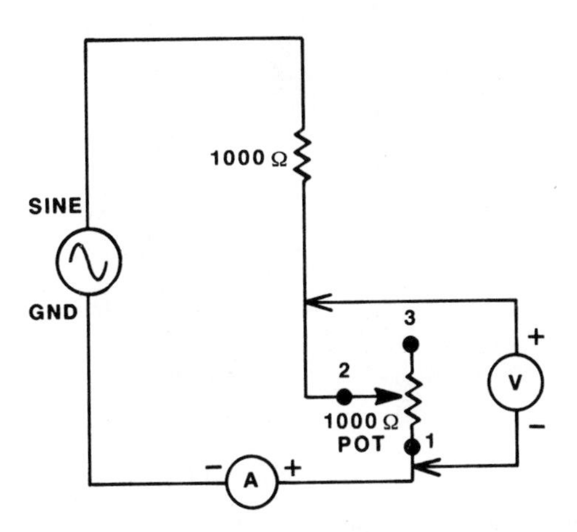

Figure E9-2
Schematic diagram of a test circuit using a fixed and variable resistor in series.

6. Switch Trainer power on, and measure the voltage drop and the current through the pot. The voltage drop across the pot is ________. The current through the pot is ________. Use Ohm's Law to calculate the pot's resistance. The calculated resistance is ________Ω.

7. Switch the Trainer power off and disconnect the pot from the circuit. Measure the pot's resistance. The resistance is ________Ω. Are the calculated and measured values equal? ________

8. Remove the ammeter and reconnect the pot to the circuit as shown in Figure E9-3. Change the position of the wiper to produce a new unknown resistance value. Connect the channel 1 input of your oscilloscope across the 1000 Ω resistor and the pot, as shown in the figure. Switch Trainer power on and record the voltage dropped across both resistors. ________ Now, use the oscilloscope to measure the voltage dropped across the pot, as shown in the figure. ________. What is the voltage dropped across the 1000 Ω resistor? ________.

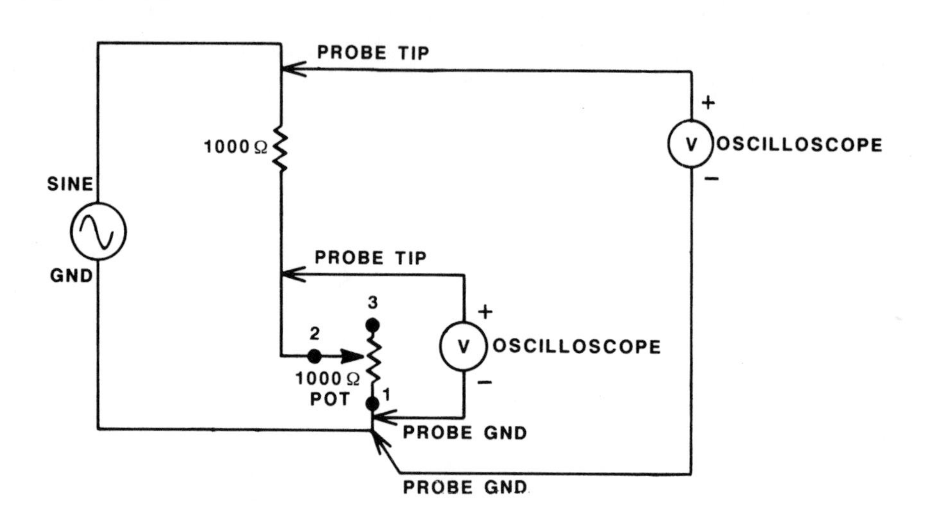

Figure E9-3

Schematic diagram of the test circuit using a fixed and variable resistor in series, and an oscilloscope connected to the circuit.

9. Calculate the current flowing through the circuit. ________ Now calculate the resistance of the pot. ________ Finally, switch Trainer power off, disconnect the pot from the circuit, and measure the unknown resistance using your ohmmeter. The measured resistance is ________Ω. Are the calculated and measured values equal? ________

Discussion

You might have noticed that the source voltage didn't stay constant as different resistances were connected. This is due to the loading effect that the resistors have on the AC voltage source of the function generator. For this exercise you should not expect to have a constant value of voltage on the output of the function generator.

In the first part of this exercise, the value of current that you measured was between 0.5 and 5.0 mA. The actual value will depend on the model Trainer you are using. However, the actual value will not affect your calculations. While your calculated voltage should be close to the measured voltage, it probably will not be exactly the same. That is due to the 5% tolerance of the resistor and the accuracy of your meters, as you learned in the earlier exercises. For example, if your measured current was 1.26 mA, then the calculated voltage would be 1.26 V. If the actual value of the resistor is 5% low (950 Ω) then the actual value of the voltage would be 1.20 V. We could also add in ammeter error and voltmeter error, but you see what we mean. The point you should remember, however, is that just as for DC circuits, you can use Ohm's Law to calculate AC voltage if the AC current and resistance are known.

Note that the value measured with your ammeter for AC current is an rms value. Therefore, the calculated voltage is also an rms value.

The second part of the exercise showed that you can use Ohm's Law to calculate an unknown resistance if the voltage and current are known. The actual values you measured will vary depending on what value of unknown resistance you set on the pot. Suppose you measured 1.83 mA of current at 0.95 V. The resistance would be 519 Ω. When you measure the resistance, you should get a value very close to your calculated value. If you didn't, try it again. The only error involved here is in the meters.

In the third part of the exercise, you used two voltage measurements and a known resistance to determine the current. Then used the calculated current along with a voltage measurement to find an unknown resistance. Again, the actual values measured will vary based on the value of the unknown resistance. If you measured 2.3 V peak-to-peak for the voltage across the 1000 Ω resistor, you can calculate the unknown current as 2.3 mA peak-to-peak. Since this is a series circuit, the current through the unknown pot resistance is the same as the current through the 1000 Ω resistor, or 2.3 mA peak-to-peak. Suppose you measure the voltage across the pot as 1.9 V peak-to-peak. The resistance of the pot can be calculated as 826 Ω. This time, the measured value may not be as close to the calculated value, since you are dealing with errors of observation, as well as calibration, on the oscilloscope and possible meter errors with the ohmmeter.

Remember that you can use peak values, peak-to-peak values, or rms values with Ohm's Law. The only restriction is that all measurements of current and voltage are made using the same method. In any calculation of voltage or current the result is expressed in the same method of measurement as the current or voltage used in the calculation. Since the measurements in the last part were made on an oscilloscope, it is convenient to express them using peak or peak-to-peak values because it is easy to make those types of measurements on the oscilloscope.

You may have noticed that in the last part, only voltage measurements were made. Measuring current requires that you somehow disconnect the circuit and insert the ammeter in the circuit. Similarly, measuring resistance requires isolating the component from the circuit. In either case, this is usually a difficult thing to do when working with a real electrical circuit and its soldered components. It is much easier to measure voltage, since this does not require modifying the circuit. By measuring the voltage drop across a known resistance, you can calculate the current without having to physically modify the circuit. Knowing the current then allows you to calculate an unknown resistance by measuring the voltage across that resistance.

Now, let's look at AC within the parallel circuit and within the complex, or series-parallel, circuit.

Procedure Continued

10. Build the circuit shown in Figure E9-4. Switch Trainer power on and use the oscilloscope to measure the voltage across resistor R2. The voltage is ________. Knowing the resistance, you can calculate the current through resistor R2 as ________. Since this is a parallel circuit, you know the current through R1 is ________. Knowing the branch currents, the source current must be ________.

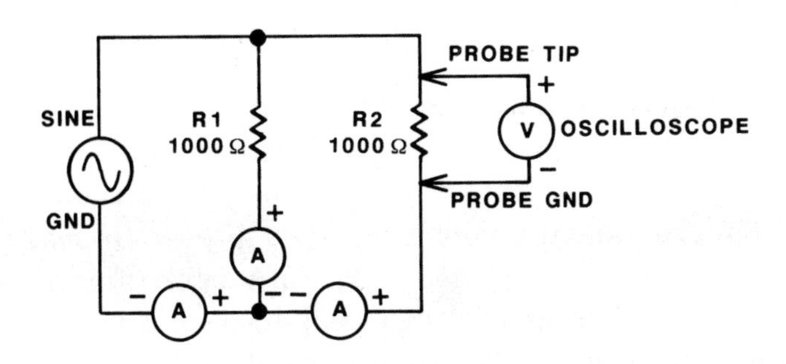

Figure E9-4
Schematic diagram of the parallel test circuit.

11. Measure the current through resistor R1, through resistor R2, and from the source. The current through R1 is ________; the current through R2 is ________; and the source current is ________. Do the measured values equal the calculated values? ________

12. Switch the Trainer power off. Build the complex circuit shown in Figure E9-5. By examining the schematic diagram, calculate the total equivalent resistance of the circuit. The total resistance is ________Ω. Switch Trainer power on. Use your voltmeter to measure the source voltage. You can now calculate the total source current as ________. Measure the source current. The current is ________. Are the currents the same? ________

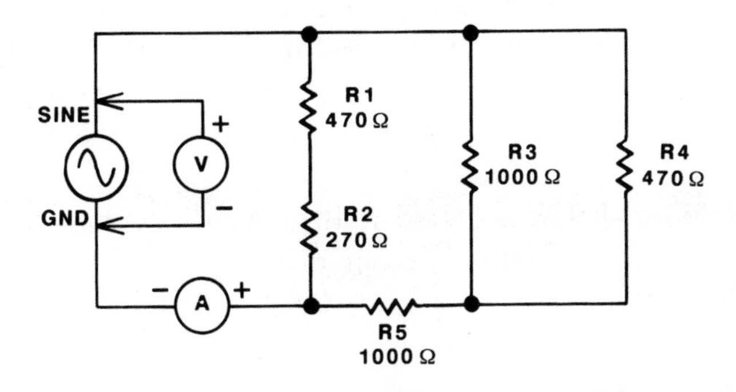

Figure E9-5
Schematic diagram of a complex circuit.

13. Calculate the voltage and current for each resistor and mark the values next to each component in the figure. Then measure each one and check your calculations. Are they the same? ________

Discussion

When you measured the voltage dropped across resistor R2, you recorded either a peak-to-peak, or a peak value. Thus, when you calculated the currents, you obtain answers using the same measurement method. For example, if you measured 2.7 V peak-to-peak across resistor R2, the current through R2 is 2.7 mA peak-to-peak. The current through resistor R1 is also 2.7 mA peak-to-peak, since it has the same resistance as resistor R2. The total current is the sum of the currents through resistors R1 and R2, or 5.4 mA peak-to-peak. The ammeter reads in rms values, so the peak-to-peak values you calculated must be converted to rms values, to make the comparison with the measured values valid. The converted branch currents equal 0.95 mA rms, while the converted total current equals 1.90 mA rms.

Measuring the actual currents using the ammeter should result in values close to the ones you calculated, but the values of current will depend on the actual values of the resistors, which could be off by up to 5%. Again you can see that the calculations are the same as for DC circuits as long as you use the same method of measurement for the voltage and current.

For the complex circuit in Figure E9-5, you should have calculated a total resistance of approximately 474 Ω. If you didn't get this value, go back and recheck your calculations. The total current is found using Ohm's Law. The value you get will depend on the source voltage of the function generator on your Trainer. The measured current should be close to your calculated value for all of the currents and voltages. If your calculated and measured values agree, you understand how to use Ohm's Law for AC circuits.

The last part of this exercise will give you a chance to see how AC and DC powers compare with each other.

Procedure Continued

14. Switch the Trainer power off. Remove all of the components from the Trainer. Construct both of the circuits shown in Figure E9-6—one on each end of the Trainer breadboard. Before you switch the Trainer on, adjust the positive DC supply knob to about 3 V, and make sure the slide switch in the AC circuit is open.

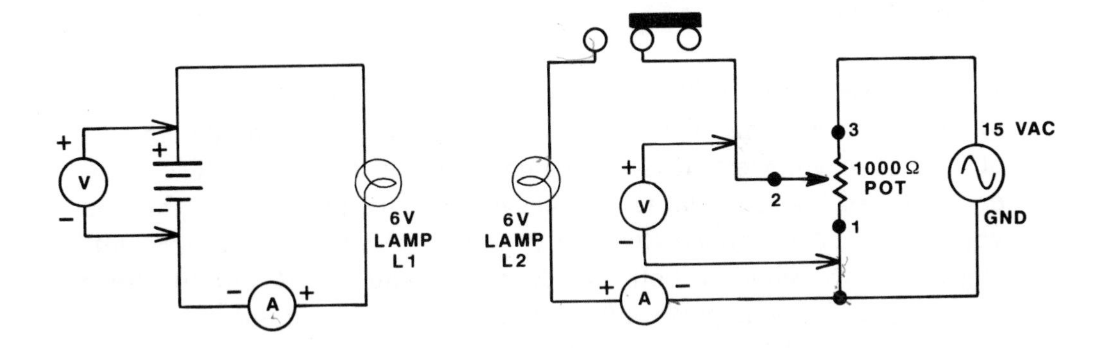

Figure E9-6

Two circuits to compare AC and DC power.

15. If you only have one voltmeter, use it in the DC circuit first. Switch the meter to DC, and connect it across the DC source. Switch the Trainer power on. Adjust the DC power supply to 4.0 V. The 6V lamp (L1) will glow, but not with its full brightness.

16. Again, if you only have one voltmeter, switch it back to AC, and connect it across the pot in the AC circuit. Adjust the wiper of the 1000 Ω pot for a reading of less than 6 V rms. Close the slide switch. At this point, the 6V lamp (L2) will not glow. That's because it's loading the circuit, thus reducing the voltage available to the lamp. Increase the AC voltage to lamp L2, by turning the wiper on the pot, until the lamp glows with exactly the same brightness as lamp L1. If you are careful with the adjustment, the two lamps are now dissipating the same amount of power. That's because it takes a certain amount of power—work per unit of time—to make the filament glow with a certain brightness.

Without changing any of the adjustments, measure the voltage and current at the indicated points in the circuit using your meter(s):

P = I × E
P = .0395 × 4
P = .158 W

The DC voltage is: 4 V.
The DC current is: 39.5 mA.
The AC voltage is: 3.97 V rms.
The AC current is: 38.8 mA rms.

10.6 p/p 5.3 p × .707 = 3.7

Calculate the power dissipated in each lamp:

The power in L1 is: .158 W.
The power in L2 is: .154 W.

P = 3.97 × .0388
P = .154 W

Discussion

The purpose of this part of the exercise is to show you that the rms method of measuring AC current and voltage does indeed give a value of current or voltage that is equivalent to a constant level DC current or voltage of the same value. If you were careful in adjusting the pot, you should have noticed that the current and voltage measurements were about the same for both the DC circuit and the AC circuit. Since you set the DC voltage to 4.0 V, the AC voltage should have been 4 V. The current for both circuits should have been close to 39 mA. Naturally, it is difficult to adjust the brightness of the lamps exactly the same, so don't feel too bad if you are off by 0.3 V, or so. Any difference in voltage will also be reflected in the two currents.

Your calculations of power in L1 and L2 should have been close to the same value, but will be different if your values of voltage and current are different. The power dissipated by each lamp is about 0.16 W.

Procedure Continued

17. This completes Exercise 9 and the exercises for Unit 4. Switch the Trainer, your oscilloscope, and your meter(s) off. Remove the wire and components from the Trainer, and save them for future exercises. Clean-up your work area.

18. Return to Unit 4 and complete the Unit Examination.

EXERCISE 10

DC Generators

PURPOSE: Demonstrate the three ingredients needed for induction.

Demonstrate DC generation using a permanent magnet DC motor.

Material Required

Trainer.
Small soldering iron (25-35 watt).
Solder.
VOM or individual DC voltmeter.
Oscilloscope.

1 100 Ω resistor (2-watt).
1 100 μF capacitor.
1 Wire coil (inductor), Heath #45-601.
1 Meter movement, Heath #407-719.
2 DC motor, Heath #420-644.
1 Magnet, Heath #474-22.
Black PVC (plastic) tubing.
#22 copper hook-up wire—red, black, and white insulation colors.

Introduction

Recall that to induce current into a conductor, you need three ingredients — the conductor, a magnetic field, and motion. Generators produce current by spinning a coiled conductor inside a magnetic field. In this exercise, you'll get a chance to observe a simple DC generator in action. But before you do that, you are going to create a little current of your own with a magnet and a conductor. Since you won't be able to generate enough current to do any work, you'll have to limit your observations to the current's effect on a meter movement and on an oscilloscope.

Procedure

1. If there is a wire shorting the terminals of the meter movement together, remove it at this time. If your meter movement doesn't already have red and black wires attached to the terminals, install the wires as follows. Cut a 6-inch red wire and a 6-inch black wire. Remove a quarter-inch of insulation from each end of each wire. Connect the red wire to the meter terminal with the plus symbol. Solder the wire to the terminal. Be careful to not overheat the terminal or you may damage the plastic meter housing. In a similar fashion, connect and solder the black wire to the other terminal.

2. While you have your soldering iron hot, check the second DC motor. If it doesn't have wires attached to its terminals, prepare and install the wires as follows. Cut a 10-inch red wire and a 10-inch black wire. Remove a quarter-inch of insulation from each end of each wire. Connect and solder the red wire to the terminal identified with a red spot of paint. Then connect and solder the black wire to the other terminal. Set the motor aside for now.

3. Build the circuit shown in Figure E10-1. Now hold the north end of magnet next to the inductor coil and move the magnet back and forth along the length of the coil. Note how the meter pointer moves up- scale and then down-scale, following the movement of the magnet. The closer you hold the magnet to the coil, the further the pointer moves. Also, the faster you move the magnet, the further the pointer moves. Why is that?

   ____

   ____

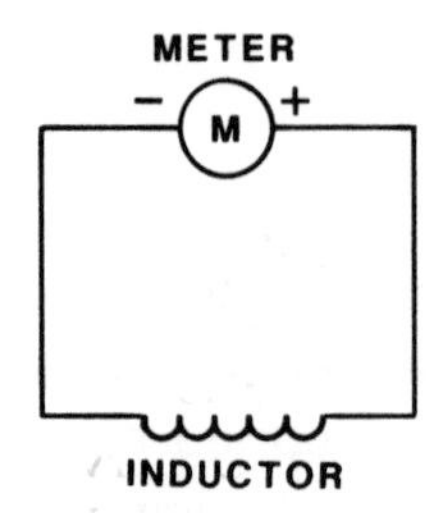

Figure E10-1
Induction test circuit.

4. Again, move the north end of the magnet back and forth along the length of the inductor coil. Note in which direction the pointer moves as you move the magnet. Now move the south end of the magnet along the length of the coil and not the direction the pointer moves. Did the direction change? ________ Why?
____
____
____

5. Connect your oscilloscope across the inductor. Set the input of the scope for about 10 mV/cm and the time base for about 10 ms/cm. Now move the north end of the magnet back and forth along the length of the inductor coil. Try to move the magnet back and forth at a fast, constant rate. You should observe a sine wave pattern on the scope. Change the speed of movement and the distance between the coil and the magnet and note any changes in the scope's display. Is this consistent with what you noted in step 3? ________ Why? ________________
____
____

Discussion

When you first examined the meter movement, you probably found a piece of wire wrapped between the terminals of the meter, shorting them together. The purpose of this wire is to protect the meter from damage during handling and shipping. By shorting the terminals together, the meter movement is actually prevented from excess movement caused by sudden jolts and jarring. You can see how this works if you recall that when a coil moves in the magnetic field of a permanent magnet, it acts like the rotor in a DC generator, generating an potential at its terminals. The shorting wire allows a current to flow between the terminals. This current creates a magnetic field around the coil which interacts with the magnetic field of the permanent magnet, resulting in a force on the coil which tends to stop the original movement. You can observe the difference the shorting wire makes by **gently** shaking the meter movement and observing the range of motion of the pointer with and without the terminals shorted. It's always a good idea to short the terminals together when you store the meter.

When you moved the magnet along the length of the coil, you were inducing a current in the coil. You could observe this in the movement of the meter pointer. You should have also noted that the closer you held the magnet to the coil and/or the faster you moved the magnet past the coil, the greater the deflection of the pointer. Did you understand why?

The first one is pretty easy. Holding the magnet closer to the coil increases the concentration of magnetic flux passing through the coil. The greater the flux, the more current that is induced. The second one takes a little more thought. Recall that current is equal to electron flow over time. Moving the magnet faster doesn't change the total number of electrons moving through the coil, but it does change the amount of time it takes to move them. Because the time is shorter, the current is greater.

Reversing the poles of the magnet reversed the direction of current flow. This has the same effect as reversing the direction of motion.

Finally, you found the oscilloscope responded just like the meter pointer, only now you can see just what the signal looks like. Did you remember, however, that you were observing a voltage signal and not a current? The meter responds to current, the way you have it connected. The scope responds to the voltage dropped across the coil, as current passes through the coil.

Procedure Continued

6. If there isn't a 1-inch piece of black PVC tubing attached to the shaft of one of your DC motors, cut off a piece and push it onto the shaft, about 1/8-inch. Now push the other end of the tube onto the shaft of the other motor. Lay the two motors in the center channel of the Trainer breadboard, near the left end.

7. Cut four 3-inch lengths of hook-up wire and remove about 1/2-inch of insulation from each end of each wire. Now use the four wires to secure the two motors to the breadboard—two wires for each motor. The wires are just long enough to wrap around the body of a motor and stick into a breadboard connector.

8. Switch Trainer power on and adjust the positive DC supply for 6 V. Then switch Trainer power off.

9. Refer to Figure E10-2 and build the circuit shown. Note that the dashed line in the schematic indicates that the output shaft of the motor is physically connected to the input shaft of the generator. Use the DC motor on the left side of the Trainer as the DC motor in your circuit and the DC motor on the right side of the Trainer as the DC generator in your circuit. Use the 1000 Ω pot on the Trainer for the variable resistor. And be sure to use the correct terminals of the pot—the red motor wire and the wire from the positive side of the power supply go to terminal 1. Turn the knob on the pot fully counterclockwise.

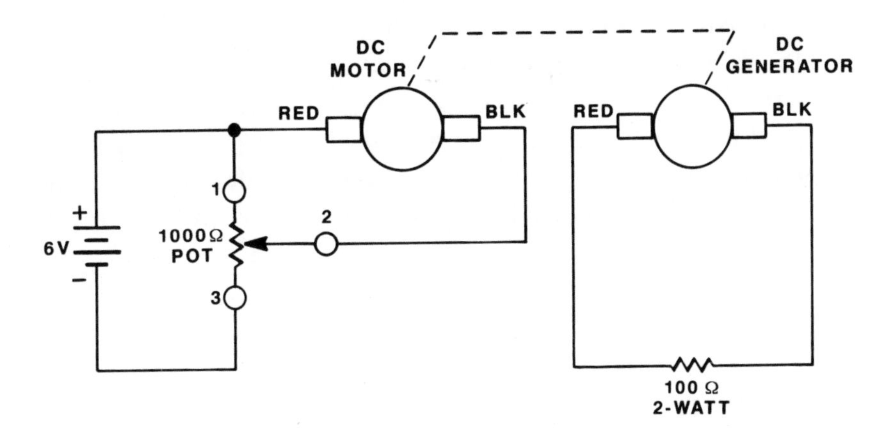

Figure E10-2
Motor/generator circuit.

10. Adjust the input of your oscilloscope for 2 V/cm and the time base for 1 ms/cm. Ground the input of your scope and center the trace. Then switch the input to DC. Connect the input of your scope across the 100 Ω resistor in your circuit. Note that the ground lead of the scope should be connected to the red-wire side of the resistor to give you a positive-going signal at the scope.

11. Switch Trainer power on. Then turn the knob of the pot until the motor starts to run. Observe the output of the generator on your scope. You should should see a series of pulses that look somewhat like one-half of a sine wave, that cycles between the ground reference and approximately 2 V. Because of the fast rise time of the signal, you may have to increase the intensity of your scope display to see the whole signal.

12. Increase the speed of the motor by turning the knob on the pot clockwise. Note what happens to the output of the generator. Reduce the speed of the motor. Again note what happens to the output of the generator. Switch Trainer power off. Describe what happened to the output of the generator, and why it happened.

____

____

____

____

13. Connect the 100 μF capacitor across the output of the generator. Make sure the negative lead of the capacitor is connected to the red-wire side of the output. Switch Trainer power on and observe the output of the generator. Vary the speed of the motor and note any changes in the output of the generator. Momentarily disconnect and then reconnect one lead of the capacitor, and note any change in the output of the generator. Switch Trainer power off. Describe the effect of the capacitor on the output of the generator.

____

____

____

Discussion

Each pulse of the generator output represents the current induced in the armature as its windings move into and out of the magnetic field of the field poles. The number of cycles-per-second is determined by the speed of rotation of the armature. Thus, as you increased the speed of the motor, the number of pulses displayed by the scope increased. At the same time, the voltage level of each pulse increased, because the armature windings were moving through the magnetic field faster.

When you connected the capacitor across the output of the generator, you "filtered" the pulses. What remained was a nearly constant DC voltage level. What little "ripple" remained varied with frequency of the generator pulses. Adding more capacitance would reduce the ripple even further.

Procedure Continued

14. Disconnect the parts and wires from the Trainer. Save them for future exercises.

15. This completes Exercise 10. Proceed to the next exercise, where you will study AC-to-DC conversion.

EXERCISE 11

AC-To-DC Conversion

PURPOSE: Demonstrate the operation of a diode.

Show how the output of an AC generator can be converted to DC using different configurations of diodes.

Material Required

Trainer.
Oscilloscope.
1 100 Ω resistor (2-watt).
1 10 kΩ resistor.
1 100 μF capacitor.
2 Silicon power diode, Heath #57-27.
White #22 copper hook-up wire.

Introduction

The AC generator is used primarily by the electric utility and nearly every automobile on the road today. The output of your Trainer's Line Frequency connector blocks represents the output of your local electric utility's AC generator. The only basic difference between the utility generator output and the Trainer output is the Trainer has transformed the voltage to two relatively safe 15 V rms outputs and one 30 V rms output. You will be using these outputs in this exercise.

Since you have already studied the various characteristics of AC, this exercise will concentrate on the conversion of AC to DC. You'll see how a diode is used to make that conversion, both as a half-wave rectifier and as a full-wave rectifier. We'll begin with a single-diode rectifier, called a half-wave rectifier.

Procedure

1. Build the circuit shown in Figure E11-1, using one of the diodes and the 10 kΩ resistor. Note that the power supply uses one of the 15 VAC connector blocks and the ground connector block of the Line Frequency section of the Trainer. Remember, the cathode end of the diode is identified by the bar in the schematic symbol and by the painted stripe on the body of the diode. Current flows through a diode from the cathode side to the anode side.

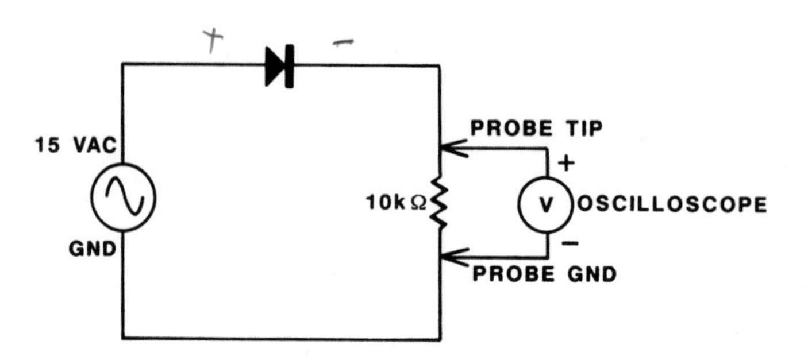

Figure E11-1
Half-wave rectifier circuit.

2. Center the trace on your oscilloscope and set the input for 10 V/cm. Adjust the time base for about 2 ms/cm. Connect the scope probe to the 15 VAC connector and the scope ground lead to the ground connector.

3. Switch Trainer power on. Note the waveform displayed by the scope. Now reconnect the scope across the "load" resistor. Again note the waveform displayed by the scope. What did the diode do to the signal? 1/2 WAVE RECTING
____

4. Switch Trainer power off. Connect the capacitor across the load resistor. Be sure the **negative** lead of the capacitor is connected to the **ground** side of the resistor. Switch the Trainer power on. Note the waveform displayed by the scope. What happend to the signal, and why did it happen? line straighten out up zero.

   Compared to the filtered DC generator signal you observed in Exercise 10, is this the type of waveform you expected? ____________

5. Switch Trainer power off. Then replace the 10 kΩ load resistor with the 100 Ω resistor.

   CAUTION: When you switch the Trainer on in the next step, don't leave it on too long. The resistor will draw about 2.25 watts of power. Since the resistor is only rated for 2 watts, it will get very hot, and could be damaged.

6. Switch Trainer power on. Note the waveform displayed by the scope. Then switch Trainer power off. Why is the signal across the 100 Ω resistor not as smooth as the signal across the 10 kΩ resistor? Cap can't keep up with current

7. Remove the capacitor, reverse the direction of the diode, and replace the 100 Ω resistor with the 10 kΩ resistor. Switch Trainer power on and note the waveform displayed by the scope. What did the diode do to the AC signal this time? 1/2 wave below zero - neg side

8. Switch Trainer power off. Again, connect the capacitor across the load resistor, only this time, be sure the **positive** lead of the capacitor is connected to the **ground** side of the resistor. Switch Trainer power on. What happened to the signal? Signal flatten out again

Discussion

Recall that the purpose of the diode in a half-wave rectifier is to block, or clip, one-half of the AC input signal. In other words, convert the AC into DC. In the first circuit that you built, you should have discovered that the negative half of the signal was clipped by the diode. Thus, your half-wave rectifier was allowing a pulsing positive DC voltage to pass.

Connecting the capacitor across the output of the rectifier filtered the pulses and produced a smooth DC voltage. However, the signal was no longer smooth when you installed the 100 Ω resistor. This is easy to understand if you remember just what the capacitor is doing.

Recall that the capacitor stores and releases electrons in response to the flow of current. The size of the capacitor determines just how many electrons it can store and release. Now in the original circuit, current flow was limited to about 1.5 mA through the 10 kΩ resistor. Because of the small amount of current, the capacitor was able to supply enough additional electrons to fill-in the empty space between the pulses. However, when the current was raised to about 150 mA, through the 100 Ω resistor, the capacitor was no longer able to keep up with the current demands of the circuit. As a result, the current pulses were not completely filled-in. Hence the large amount of ripple you observed on the scope.

Reversing the diode caused it to clip the positive half of the signal. The result was a pulsing negative DC voltage. As before, you were able to filter those pulses with the capacitor.

Did you understand why you had to install the capacitor backwards when you reversed the direction of current flow? It has to do with the construction of the capacitor. While many of the smaller types of capacitors are not polarized, most of the larger types, like the electrolytic in this exercise, are polarized. This method of construction demands that current flow into and out of the capacitor in a specific direction. Since your diode rectifier was producing a negative voltage, you had to connect the positive lead of the capacitor to ground, because that point had the most positive potential in the circuit.

If you reverse the direction of current flow in a polarized capacitor, you will damage the capacitor. At best, that means shortening the life of the capacitor. At worst, that means causing the capacitor to short-out or possibly burst.

Procedure Continued

9. Switch Trainer power off. Refer to Figure E11-2 and modify the circuit on your Trainer breadboard as shown. Note that you are now using the 30 VAC output from the Trainer, and that the load resistor is connected between the output of the rectifier circuit and AC ground.

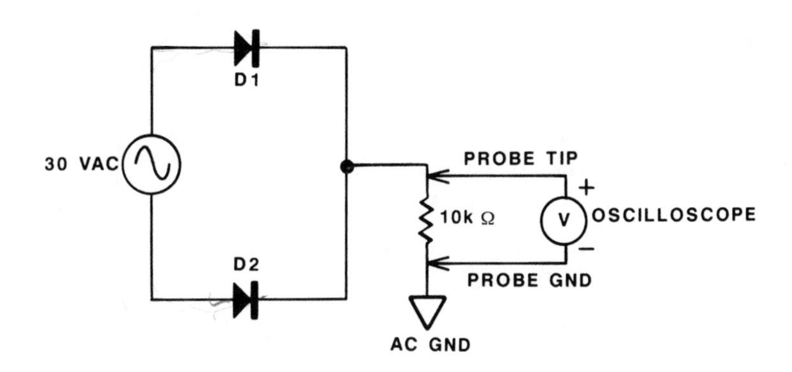

Figure E11-2

Full-wave rectifier circuit.

10. Switch Trainer power on and note the waveform displayed by the scope. How does it differ from the waveform generated by a half-wave rectifier? Retifing neg wave to pos

    Why does the full-wave rectifier generate this type of waveform?
    All the sig. same direction

11. Switch Trainer power off and connect the capacitor across the load resistor. Be sure to connect the positive lead of the capacitor to the junction of diodes D1, D2, and the resistor. Switch Trainer power on and note the waveform displayed by the scope. Is it what you expected? yes Why is there essentially no ripple in the DC voltage? NOT AS much AREA TO rectified between waves

12. Switch Trainer power off. Replace the 10 kΩ load resistor with the 100 Ω resistor. Switch Trainer power on and note the waveform displayed by the scope, then immediately switch Trainer power off. Is there as much ripple in the waveform as you noted in the half-wave rectifier circuit you constructed earlier? Less Why do you think that is the case? less to fill in between wave

Discussion

The waveform produced by a full-wave rectifier differs from that produced by a half-wave rectifier because there are no gaps between the current pulses. There are no gaps because both halves of the AC signal are used to generate the DC signal. During the positive cycle of the AC cycle, current flows through the load resistor and diode D2; and during the negative half of the AC cycle, current flows through the load resistor and diode D1. That's because the 30 VAC transformer acted just like two 15 VAC transformers connected to the same ground point (see Page 87). The diodes cause each transformer to conduct on alternate halves of the AC cycle. As a result, current always flows through the resistor in the same direction.

As you should have guessed, the voltage dropped across the 10 kΩ load resistor and the capacitor was essentially ripple-free. However, there was a lot of ripple when you substituted the 100 Ω resistor. Again, the capacitor didn't have the capacity to supply enough electrons to fill-in the area between the pulses. On the other hand, there was less ripple than you experienced with the half-wave rectifier circuit. That's because there wasn't as much area to fill between the pulses with the full-wave rectifier circuit.

Procedure Continued

13. This completes Exercise 11 and the exercises for Unit 5. Switch your oscilloscope off. Remove the wire and components from the Trainer, and save them for future exercises. Clean-up your work area.

14. Return to Unit 5 and complete the Unit Examination.

EXERCISE 12

The d'Arsonval Meter Movement And The DC Ammeter

PURPOSE: Demonstrate the physical construction of the permanent-magnet moving-coil meter movement.

Show how to use the meter movement to construct a simple DC ammeter and how to test its operation.

Demonstrate experimentally, the effect of ammeter insertion loss.

Show how the meter movement is used to construct a simple AC ammeter.

Material Required

Trainer.
VOM or individual DC ammeter, DC voltmeter, and AC ammeter.
Small soldering iron (25-35 watt).
Solder.
1 3 Ω resistor.
1 27 Ω resistor.
1 100 Ω resistor (2 Watt).
1 270 Ω resistor.
2 470 Ω resistor.
1 5600 Ω resistor.
1 12 kΩ resistor.
1 100 kΩ pot (to replace ET-3600 pot)*.
2 Signal diode, Heath #56-89.
1 Meter movement, Heath #407-719.
#22 copper hook-up wire—red, black, and white insulation colors

* If you are using a modified ET-3600 Analog Trainer, you have also been using a separate 1000 Ω pot in place of the pot on the Trainer. In this and the remaining exercises, you must also substitute the 100 kΩ pot on the Trainer with the 100 kΩ pot supplied with the circuit parts.

Introduction

You have been using your AC and DC ammeters for measuring current and you should be familiar with their operation. You may, however, have wondered what the circuit on the inside of the ammeter is like. This exercise is designed to show you how an analog ammeter works. First you will examine the construction and electrical characteristics of a permanent-magnet moving-coil meter movement. Then you will use the meter movement to build simple AC and DC ammeters and use them to measure the current in AC and DC circuits. In the next two exercises, you will build a voltmeter and an ohmmeter using the same meter movement.

Procedure

1. Find the meter movement included in your parts pack. Notice that the meter face is protected with a clear plastic cover that is held in place with tape. In order to examine the movement, **carefully** remove the tape and lift off the plastic cover. Examine the construction of the meter magnet, coil, and pointer.

2. Locate the permanent magnet. In this case the core in the center of the coil is the permanent magnet. Note that there is a soft iron frame around the outside of the coil to provide a path for the magnetic field. The coil itself is wound on an aluminum (non-magnetic) coil form which holds the shape of the coil and allows it to freely rotate around the core. The pointer is balanced by a small metal plate on the opposite side of the coil from the pointer. Find the adjustment lever for the pointer and carefully adjust it so that the pointer rests exactly over zero on the scale. Look closely at how the adjustment lever is connected to the spiral spring on the front of the coil assembly. Carefully replace the cover on the meter movement and secure it in place with a piece of tape. NOTE: There may be a small opening in the front of the cover to allow you to reach the zero adjustment lever without having to remove the cover again.

3. If there is a wire shorting the terminals of the meter movement together, remove it at this time. The ends of the red and black meter wires may be twisted together.

NOTE: The specifications for the meter movement are: 200 μA full-scale current and a coil resistance of 1200 Ω. Refer to the circuit in Figure E12-1. The symbol that is a circle with the letter "M" inside of it represents the meter movement. The other meter symbols are the same as in the earlier exercises.

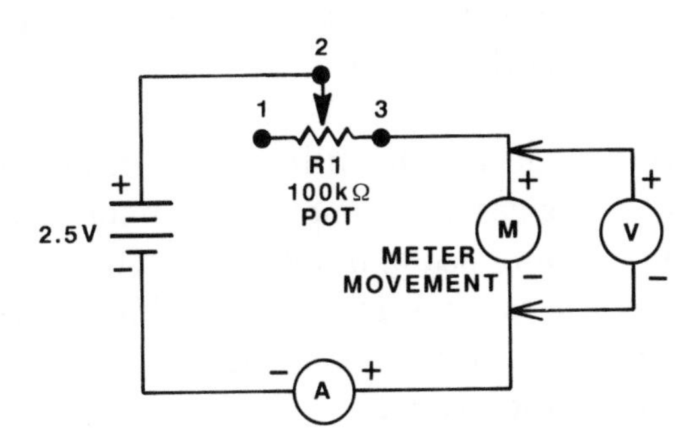

Figure E12-1

Circuit to measure meter movement characteristics.

4. Switch the Trainer power on. Connect a DC voltmeter to the output of the positive DC power supply, and adjust the supply to 2.5 V. Switch Trainer power off and build the circuit shown in Figure E12-1. Adjust the wiper of the 100 kΩ pot to about the center of its rotation. Switch Trainer power on. Adjust the 100 kΩ pot until the meter movement indicates full-scale deflection—the pointer is aligned with the 10 on the scale.

5. Measure the circuit current. It is ________mA. Now measure the voltage drop across the meter movement. It is ________V. Calculate the resistance of the meter coil. The calculated meter coil resistance is ________Ω. Do your results match the specifications for the meter? ________.

6. Adjust the pot until the measured current through the meter movement is one-half the value measured for the full-scale current—about 100 μA. Record the reading on the meter movement: ________.

7. Switch the Trainer power off.

Discussion

Measuring the characteristics of your meter movement requires some careful thought before any measurements are made. If you use your ohmmeter to measure the resistance of the meter coil you will most likely force too much current through the meter coil, possibly damaging the meter. However, it is possible to measure the current through the meter movement and the voltage across it. Then you can use Ohm's Law to calculate the meter coil resistance.

The measurement you made at 50% full-scale current indicates how linear (or non-linear in this case!) the meter movement is. If you didn't get a reading of 5 on the meter scale, don't panic. The meter movement included in the course parts pack is relatively inexpensive and it is not designed to be very linear. Remember this when you make readings for the subsequent parts of the exercise.

Procedure Continued

8. Refer to Figure E12-2. This is a multirange ammeter circuit with full-scale ranges of 1, 10, and 100 mA. Using the specifications for your meter movement, try to calculate the required values for the shunt resistors. The calculations are described on the following page.

   R2 = ____________Ω
   R3 = ____________Ω
   R4 = ____________Ω

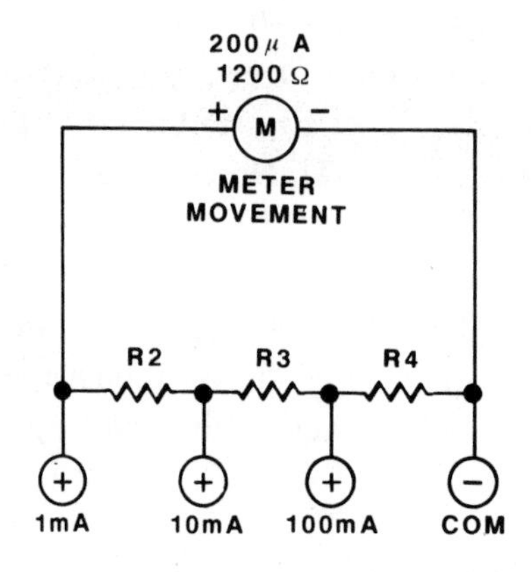

Figure E12-2
Multirange ammeter circuit.

Discussion

With full-scale current through the meter movement, the voltage drop across the meter coil is 0.24 V. When the 1 mA range is connected, the three shunt resistors are in series, and can be treated as a single shunt resistor. If the total current through the meter circuit is 1 mA, and 200 μA flows through the meter coil, then the current through the shunt is 0.8 mA. With this information, the total shunt resistance is easily calculated using Ohm's Law. It equals 300 Ω.

Now the process becomes less obvious, because you have more than one unknown quantity when you consider the 10 mA and 100 mA ranges. For the 10 mA range, R2 is in series with the meter movement, which increases the resistance in that branch, while R3 and R4 form a shunt around the meter movement and R2. At the full-scale current of 10 mA, the current through R3 and R4 is 9.8 mA, but you don't know the voltage across them because you don't know the resistance of R2 yet. The easy way to arrive at a value for R2 is to begin by assuming a value for the voltage across R2. Knowing the voltage across R2 allows you to find the voltage across R3 and R4 by subtraction. Then you can calculate the total resistance of R3 + R4 using Ohm's Law. Subtract this result from the total shunt resistance to find a resistance value for R2. Now you can find the voltage drop across R2, and check how close your original guess was. Most likely the first guess wasn't very close, so you'll need to refine the guess by repeating the process using the new value for the voltage across R2. Usually two or three repetitions are sufficient to reach an accurate value.

For example, if you initially assume the voltage across R2 is zero, you know that the voltage across R3 + R4 is the same as the voltage across the meter movement, which is 0.24 V. Then it is easy to calculate the total resistance of R3 + R4. Subtract this value from the total shunt resistance (300 Ω) to find the resistance of R2. Now that you have a resistance value for R2, you can repeat the process. First, find the voltage across the meter movement and R2 at full-scale current. Then using that information, recalculate the value of R3 + R4, and so on. With this method, you should arrive at a value of about 270 Ω for R2 and 30 Ω for R3 + R4. You can then follow a similar procedure to determine that the value for R3 is about 27 Ω and and that the value for R4 is about 3 Ω. Now, you can use these resistance values to build a multi-range ammeter.

Procedure Continued

9. Refer to Figure E12-2 and write the value 270 Ω next to resistor R2. Then write the value 27 Ω next to resistor R3. Finally, write the value 3 Ω next to resistor R4. Now build the ammeter circuit shown in the figure. For the rest of this exercise this ammeter circuit will be called your "breadboard ammeter." To help avoid confusion, we'll call your instrument DC ammeter a "DC ammeter."

10. Switch the Trainer power on. Connect a DC voltmeter to the output of the positive DC power supply, and adjust the supply to 10 V. Do not change this setting until instructed to do so. Switch the Trainer power off.

11. To test the accuracy of your breadboard ammeter, construct the circuit shown in Figure E12-3. Note that the two pots in the circuit are the 1000 Ω and 100 kΩ pots on the Trainer. Wire the breadboard ammeter into the circuit using the **10 mA** and **COM** connection points. Adjust the wipers of pots R5 and R6 to the center of their range.

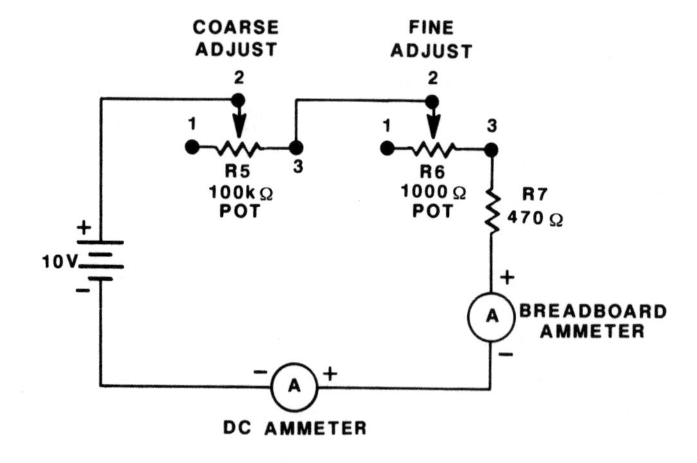

Figure E12-3
Circuit to test the breadboard DC ammeter.

12. Switch the Trainer power on. Adjust the course and fine adjust pots, R5 and R6, for a reading of 2 mA on your breadboard ammeter. Record the reading of you DC ammeter in the "measured current" column of Figure E12-4. In like manner, adjust the current and record the measured value for the 4, 6, 8, and 10 mA current values in Figure E12-4. When you finish, adjust the pots for minimum current—less than 1 mA. Note that you will fill-in the "1 mA range" readings in the next step.

BREADBOARD AMMETER CURRENT	MEASURED CURRENT	PERCENT ERROR
2 mA		
4 mA		
6 mA		
8 mA		
10 mA		
0.2 mA		
0.4 mA		
0.6 mA		
0.8 mA		
1 mA		

Figure E12-4
Chart of breadboard ammeter characteristics.

13. Switch the Trainer power off. Pull the wire going to the **10 mA** connection point on the breadboard ammeter and plug it into the **1 mA** connection point on the breadboard ammeter. Switch the Trainer power on and adjust the pots for a reading of 0.2 mA on the breadboard ammeter. Record the reading of you DC ammeter in the "measured current" column of Figure E12-4. As before, adjust the current and record the measured value for the 0.4, 0.6, 0.8, and 1 mA current values in Figure E12-4. When you finish, adjust the pots for minimum current and switch the Trainer power off.

14. Calculate the percent error for each reading you recorded in Figure E12-4. Use the following equation to make the calculation:

$$\%\ \text{ERROR} = \frac{\text{BREADBOARD AMMETER CURRENT} - \text{MEASURED CURRENT}}{\text{MEASURED CURRENT}} \times 100\%$$

15. Now that you have established the accuracy of your breadboard ammeter, it's time to determine it's insertion loss characteristics.

    First, calculate the total resistance of the circuit in Figure E12-3 if the current is 10 mA and none of the ammeters are in the circuit. The resistance is ______Ω. Next, calculate the resistance of the circuit in Figure E12-2, if it is used as a 10 mA ammeter. The 10 mA ammeter circuit resistance is ________Ω. Now assume the 10 mA ammeter is reinserted into the circuit in Figure E12-3. What is the circuit current? ________mA

16. To test your answer, remove the breadboard ammeter from the circuit on the Trainer. (The easy way to do this is to short the leads of the breadboard ammeter together.) Switch the Trainer power on and adjust the two pots until the DC ammeter indicates a current of 10 mA. Without changing the resistance of the pots, reinsert the breadboard ammeter (10 mA range) into the circuit. What is the actual current reading on your DC ammeter? ________mA

17. Without changing anything else, switch the Trainer power off. Then change the input to the breadboard ammeter to the 100 mA range. What is the current reading from the DC ammeter? __________mA

Discussion

You probably noticed that at the full-scale values of 1.0 mA and 10 mA the breadboard ammeter is fairly accurate. If the percent error at full-scale is greater than 10%, you should go back and check for mistakes. At mid-scale, however, you may have as much as 35% error! There are two major reasons for this error. First of all, the meter movement supplied in your parts pack is not really intended for accurate measurements. Due to its inherent non-linearity, it may be in error as much as 30% at mid-scale. The other source of error is the tolerance of the resistors used. Since these are 5% tolerance resistors, they may cause an additional error of up to 5%.

With a 10 V source, the total resistance must be adjusted to 1000 Ω to cause 10 mA of current to flow. The breadboard ammeter has an internal resistance of about 30 Ω in the 10 mA range (30 Ω in parallel with 1470 Ω). Therefore, when the breadboard ammeter is inserted in the circuit, the total circuit resistance increases to 1030 Ω. Now the resulting current is 9.71 mA. The loss of 0.29 mA is due to insertion loss in the breadboard ammeter. In the 100 mA range, the internal resistance is only about 3 Ω, and therefore it has almost no effect on the circuit current. Of course, at one-tenth scale, the meter isn't very accurate, but at least the insertion loss is decreased! Obviously there is a trade-off between insertion loss and ammeter accuracy.

The reason the 100 mA range is not tested, is because the Trainer pots will not tolerate that much current without possible damage due to overheating. It is the purpose of the 470 Ω series resistor to limit the current to a safe level. You can, however, test the 100 mA range with a different circuit. The following steps show you how.

Procedure Continued

18. Switch the Trainer power off. Remove the two pots and resistor from the original test circuit, and replace them with a 100 Ω, 2-watt resistor, as shown in Figure E12-5. Make sure the breadboard ammeter is still set-up for a 100 mA input range. Change the DC ammeter input to the 100 mA range. Finally, turn the positive DC power supply voltage control to **minimum**. You will use this control to regulate the current in the circuit.

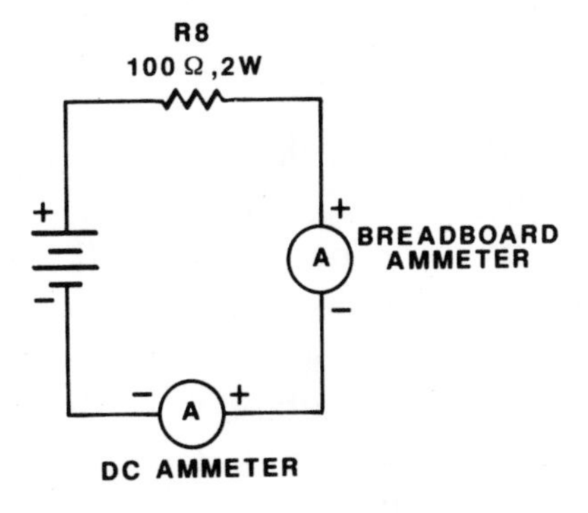

Figure E12-5
Circuit to test the 100 mA DC range.

19. Switch the Trainer power on. Adjust the DC power supply output to produce a 20 mA reading on the breadboard ammeter. Record the DC ammeter reading in the "measured current" column in Figure E12-6. As before, adjust the current and record the measured value for the 40, 60, 80, and 100 mA current values in Figure E12-6. Make these measurements quickly—the 100 Ω resistor will get hot to the touch. When you finish, adjust the DC power supply for minimum voltage and switch the Trainer power off. Allow the resistor to cool.

BREADBOARD AMMETER CURRENT	MEASURED CURRENT	PERCENT ERROR
20 mA		
40 mA		
60 mA		
80 mA		
100 mA		

Figure E12-6
Chart of 100 mA breadboard ammeter characteristics.

20. Calculate the percent error for each reading you recorded in Figure E12-6.

Discussion

If you leave the full-scale current flowing through the circuit very long the 100 Ω resistor will get hot to the touch, and may even get hot enough to burn your fingers. The resistor will not be damaged, since it is a 2 W resistor and the power dissipation is only 1 W with 100 mA of current. You should see, however, that it is important that you take into account the power limitations of the components used in circuits that you work with or build. This is something that is easy to overlook if you are not careful.

The values you obtained for "percent error" should be comparable to the values you obtained for the other ranges of the breadboard ammeter.

In the last part of this exercise, you will briefly examine an AC ammeter circuit by building a single-range 1 mA, full-scale AC ammeter.

Procedure Continued

21. Build the AC ammeter circuit shown in Figure E12-7. Then add it to the circuit shown in Figure E12-8. Make sure your instrument ammeter is set to measure AC current on the 1 mA range. As in the earlier test circuit, the two pots are located on the Trainer. Rotate the wipers of pots R12 and R13 to about the center of their range.

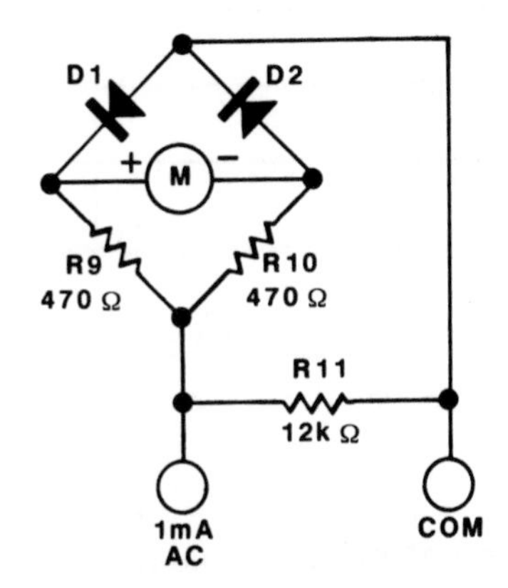

Figure E12-7
Simple AC ammeter.

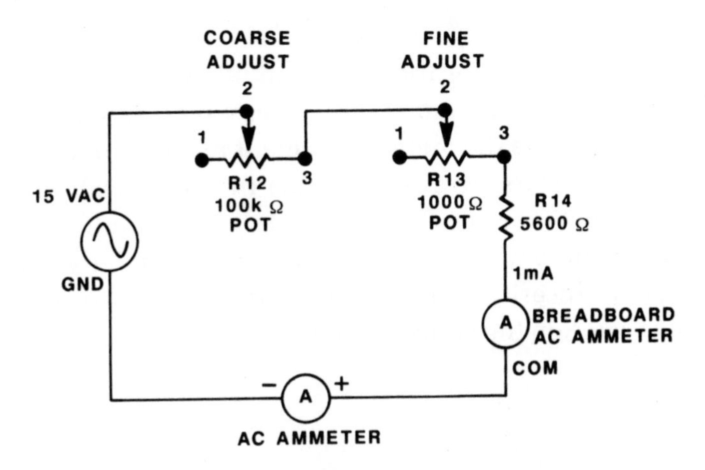

Figure E12-8
Circuit to test the breadboard AC ammeter.

22. Switch the Trainer power on. Adjust the two pots for a reading of 0.2 mA AC on the breadboard AC ammeter. Record the AC ammeter reading in the "measured current" column in Figure E12-9. As before, adjust the current and record the measured value for the 0.4, 0.6, 0.8, and 1 mA AC current values in Figure E12-9. Then switch the Trainer power off.

BREADBOARD AMMETER CURRENT	MEASURED CURRENT	PERCENT ERROR
0.2 mA		
0.4 mA		
0.6 mA		
0.8 mA		
1 mA		

Figure E12-9

Chart of breadboard AC ammeter characteristics.

23. Calculate the percent error for each reading you recorded in Figure E12-9.

Discussion

Recall that the presence of the diode circuit in an AC ammeter causes some non-linearity in the ammeter scale, which explains some of the mid-scale error. Since the meter movement itself is not accurate at mid-scale, and the resistors are also not exact in value, the mid-scale values show more than 35% error. The full-scale value should be closer, since the meter is more accurate here. On commercially available AC ammeters, non-linearity of the AC measurement is corrected by printing a non-linear scale on the ammeter face.

Procedure Continued

24. Remove the wire and components from the Trainer breadboard and save them for future exercises. Remember to short the terminals of the meter movement. Put your soldering iron away and clean-up your work area.

25. This completes Exercise 12. Proceed to the next exercise, where you will study the characteristics of the voltmeter.

EXERCISE 13

The Voltmeter

PURPOSE: Show how to use a permanent-magnet moving-coil meter movement to construct a simple DC voltmeter, and how to test its operation.

Demonstrate experimentally, the effects of voltmeter loading.

Demonstrate how the meter movement is used to construct a simple AC voltmeter.

Show how to experimentally calibrate a meter.

Material Required

Trainer.
VOM or individual DC voltmeter and AC voltmeter.

1 Meter movement, Heath #407-719
2 470 Ω resistor.
1 1000 Ω resistor.
1 2000 Ω resistor.
1 3830 Ω resistor.
2 10 kΩ resistor.
1 45.3 kΩ resistor.
1 100 kΩ resistor.
2 Signal diode, Heath # 56-89.
White #22 copper hook-up wire.

Introduction

The moving-coil meter movement can be used to measure voltage if you add the appropriate multiplier resistors. In this exercise you will calculate the resistance values required for a simple 3-range DC voltmeter and then build the meter circuit. Next you will compare the response of this breadboard voltmeter with the response of your instrument DC voltmeter. Then you will examine the effect of voltmeter loading on a circuit. Finally, you will build an AC voltmeter, test the voltmeter, and construct a calibrated scale for the voltmeter.

Procedure

1. Refer to Figure E13-1. This is the circuit diagram for a simple 3-range DC voltmeter with full-scale ranges of 1, 10, and 30 V. Using the specifications for your meter movement, try to calculate the values for the three multiplier resistors. The calculations are described on the following page.

   R1 = ________Ω
   R2 = ________Ω
   R3 = ________Ω

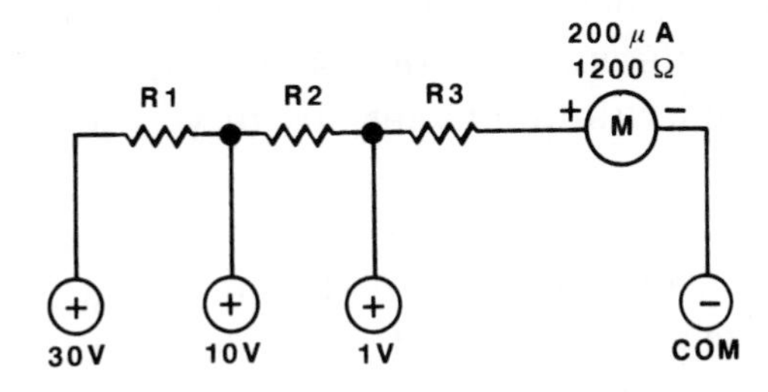

Figure E13-1
Three-range DC voltmeter circuit.

Discussion

The total resistance of the voltmeter circuit in any range must be such that when the full-scale voltage is applied to the terminals, full-scale current flows through the meter movement. To determine the individual resistor values, first calculate the total resistance of the circuit. Then subtract the meter coil resistance and the other known resistances. If you start with the 1 V range, it is a simple calculation, since there is only one resistor in the circuit. You know that in the 1 V range, the total resistance must be sufficient to allow 200 μA of current to flow when the terminal voltage is 1 V. Through Ohm's Law, you know that total meter circuit resistance must be 5000 Ω. Since the meter coil itself has a resistance of 1200 Ω, that leaves 3800 Ω for resistor R3.

In the 10 V range, the total resistance must be 50 kΩ. The meter circuit now contains resistors R2 and R3, and the meter movement. To find the value of resistor R2, simply subtract the value of resistor R3 and the meter coil from 50 kΩ. That leaves a resistance of 45 kΩ for resistor R2. Similarly, the value for R1 is calculated as 100 kΩ.

Procedure Continued

2. Refer to Figure E13-1 and write the value 100 kΩ next to resistor R1. Then write the value 45.3 kΩ next to resistor R2. Finally, write the value 3830 Ω next to resistor R3. Note that these values are slightly different from the calculated values. However, they will work well with the meter circuit you will build in the next step.

3. Build the DC voltmeter circuit shown in Figure E13-1. We'll call this circuit your "breadboard voltmeter," and we'll call your instrument DC voltmeter simply a "DC voltmeter." Your breadboard voltmeter can now be used to measure DC voltages between 0 and 30 V.

4. Switch the Trainer power on. Connect a DC voltmeter to the output of the positive DC power supply, and adjust the supply to 12 V. Do not change this setting until instructed to do so. Switch the Trainer power off.

5. To test the accuracy of your breadboard voltmeter, construct the circuit shown in Figure E13-2. Use the 1000 Ω pot on the Trainer. Wire the breadboard voltmeter into the circuit using the **1 V** and **COM** connection points. Turn the pot wiper fully counterclockwise, so the voltmeters will see minimum voltage when power is switched on.

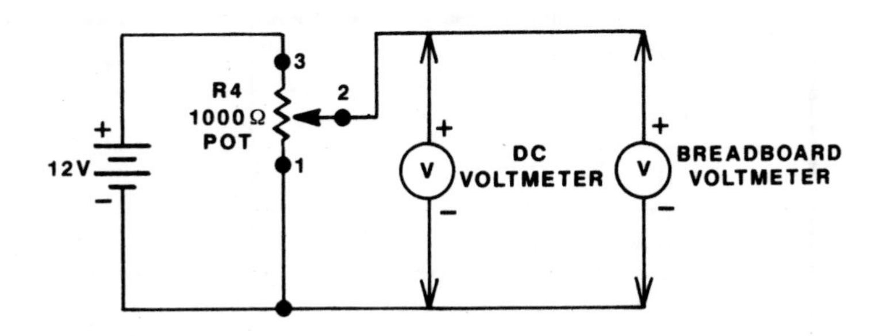

Figure E13-2
Circuit to test the 1 V and 10 V ranges.

6. Switch the Trainer Power on. Adjust pot R4 for a reading of 0.2 V on your breadboard voltmeter. Record the reading of you DC voltmeter in the "measured voltage" column of Figure E13-3. In like manner, adjust the voltage with the pot and record the measured value for the 0.4, 0.6, 0.8, and 1 V voltage values in Figure 13-3.

BREADBOARD VOLTMETER VOLTAGE	MEASURED VOLTAGE	PERCENT ERROR
0.2 V		
0.4 V		
0.6 V		
0.8 V		
1 V		
2 V		
4 V		
6 V		
	7.5 V	—
8 V		
10 V		

Figure E13-3

Chart of breadboard voltmeter characteristics.

7. Switch the Trainer power off. Reconnect the breadboard voltmeter to the test circuit so it has a 10-volt range.

8. Switch the Trainer power on. Adjust pot R4 for a reading of 2 V on your breadboard voltmeter. Record the reading of you DC voltmeter in the "measured voltage" column of Figure E13-3. As before, adjust the voltage with the pot and record the measured value for the 4, 6, 8, and 10 V voltage values in Figure 13-3. Then adjust the voltage to an actual 7.5 V and record the reading on the breadboard voltmeter in the Figure E13-3. When you finish, switch the Trainer power off.

9. Calculate the percent error for each reading (except 7.5 V) that you recorded in Figure E13-3. Use the following equation to make the calculation:

$$\% \text{ ERROR} = \frac{\text{BREADBOARD VOLTMETER VOLTAGE–MEASURED CURRENT}}{\text{MEASURED VOLTAGE}} \times 100\%$$

10. In order to test the 30 V range of your breadboard voltmeter, you must combine the capacity of both the positive and negative DC power supplies on the Trainer. Figure E13-4 shows how you use the power supplies. Adjust the controls of both power supplies to their minimum voltage settings. Then connect the two voltmeters to the power supplies as shown in the figure. Be sure to use the 30-volt configuration when you connect your breadboard voltmeter.

CAUTION: If your DC voltmeter negative lead is connected to chassis ground, you must isolate the meter from the AC ground on the power cord. Otherwise, you will cause excessive current to flow when you connect the negative supply to the negative lead on the DC voltmeter. (Note that the ground connection shown between the positive and negative supplies, in the figure, is inside your Trainer.) You can isolate your DC voltmeter by operating it on battery power (if so equipped), operating it through an isolation transformer, or by plugging it into a three-to-two-prong AC plug adapter.

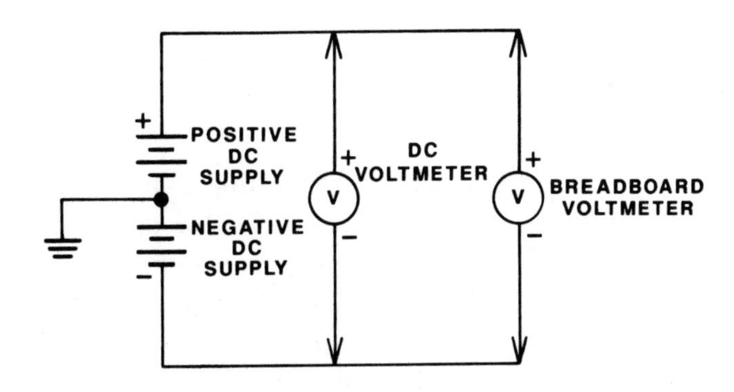

Figure E13-4

Meter connections to test the 30 VDC range.

11. Switch the Trainer power on. Adjust the two power supply controls for a reading of 6 volts on your breadboard voltmeter. Record the reading of your DC voltmeter in the "measured voltage" column of Figure E13-5. As before, adjust the voltage and record the measured value for the 12, 18, 24, and 30 V voltage values in Figure E13-5. When you finish, return the two power supply controls to their minimum voltage settings. Then switch the Trainer power off.

BREADBOARD VOLTMETER VOLTAGE	MEASURED VOLTAGE	PERCENT ERROR
6 V		
12 V		
18 V		
24 V		
30 V		

Figure E13-5
Continuation of the chart of breadboard voltmeter characteristics.

12. Again, calculate the percent error for each reading you recorded in Figure E13-5.

Discussion

The DC power supply in your Trainer can be adjusted to about 1.2 V minimum. To get a lower voltage, for checking the breadboard voltmeter in the 1 V full-scale range, you needed a "voltage divider." We had you use the 1000 Ω pot on the Trainer in that capacity. As Figure E13-2 shows, a voltage is applied across the ends of the pot. The wiper then "taps" a portion of that voltage for the voltmeters.

You would probably agree that the breadboard voltmeter you have built isn't perfect, but it does give you an idea of how a voltmeter works. The full-scale readings should be within 10% of the actual value. The error near mid-scale is again due to the non-linearity of the meter movement and resistor tolerance error. Note, however, that although the circuit resistor values for R2 and R3 are different from what you calculated, they are still within 5% of the calculated values. That's because those resistors have a 1% tolerance. Compare the breadboard voltmeter errors with the breadboard ammeter errors in the last exercise, and you should find that they are similar.

The 7.5 V reading that you recorded will be used as a reference in a later step.

Procedure Continued

13. Remove the wires going to the 1000 Ω pot on the Trainer. Do not disassemble your breadboard voltmeter circuit.

14. To observe the effect of voltmeter loading, build the two-resistor circuit shown in Figure E13-6, but do not connect the voltmeters to the circuit. Switch the Trainer power on. Then monitor the output of the positive DC power supply with the DC voltmeter and adjust the output for 15 V.

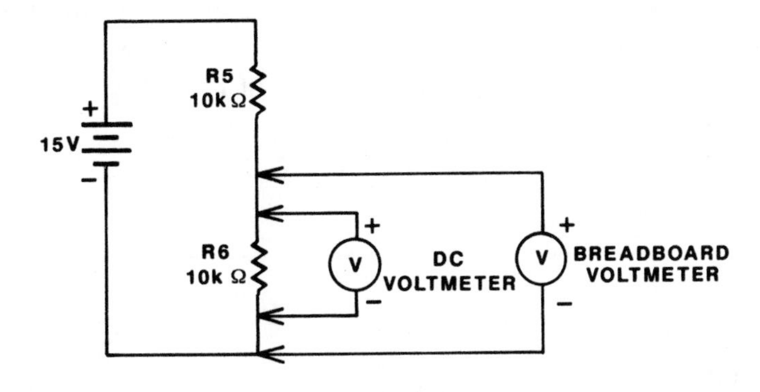

Figure E13-6
Circuit to study voltmeter loading.

15. Calculate the voltage drop across resistor R6. It is ________V. Now calculate the internal resistance of your breadboard voltmeter in the 10 V range. It is ________Ω. Finally, calculate the voltage drop across resistor R6 if your breadboard voltmeter (10 V range) is connected across the resistor. It is ________V.

16. Connect your DC voltmeter across resistor R6, as shown in Figure E13- 6. The voltage dropped across the resistor is ________V. Leave your DC voltmeter connected and connect your breadboard voltmeter (10 V range) across resistor R6. The breadboard voltmeter reads ________V. Now, the DC voltmeter reads ________V. How much did the voltage change due to loading by the breadboard voltmeter? ________V

17. Switch the Trainer power off. Replace your 1000 Ω resistors with 470 Ω resistors. Switch the Trainer power on and repeat the calculations and measurements as follows: The calculated voltage drop across R6 is now ________V. The calculated voltage drop across R6 with the breadboard voltmeter connected (10 V range) is now ________V. The measured voltage dropped across resistor R6 with the breadboard voltmeter disconnected is now ________V. The measured voltage dropped across resistor R6 with the breadboard voltmeter connected is now ________V. The voltage read by the breadboard voltmeter is now ________V. The amount of change due to breadboard voltmeter loading is now ________V. Explain the difference in the final results of this step as compared with that in step 16: ____

____

____

____

Discussion

With a 15 V source voltage, the calculated voltage drop across resistor R6 is 7.5 V, since resistors R5 and R6 are the same value and in series. Because the internal resistance of your DC voltmeter is probably much greater than the resistance of R6, you should have measured about 7.5 V across resistor R6. This value may vary as much as 5% due to resistor tolerance error.

The internal resistance of the breadboard voltmeter in the 10 V range is the sum of the resistances in the meter circuit when the 10 V range is connected. This is the resistance of resistors R2, plus R3, plus the meter coil resistance. When this resistance is connected in parallel with resistor R6, the 10 kΩ resistor, the effective resistance is 8342 Ω.

With the breadboard voltmeter connected across resistor R6, the calculated voltage drop is 6.82 V. You should have measured a voltage drop of about 6.8 V across resistor R6 with the breadboard voltmeter connected. Again, the actual reading will depend on resistor tolerance error and any "slight" loading on the part of your DC voltmeter. The reading on the breadboard voltmeter may not be the same, but should indicate a reduction from the value recorded for the 7.5 V setting in Figure E13-3. Loading by the breadboard voltmeter causes about a 10% reduction of the voltage across resistor R6. This may not seem to be a large error, but it is unacceptable for most applications. On the other hand, a 10% error might inadvertently go unnoticed in many cases unless you are aware of the effects of voltmeter loading.

Remember that voltmeter loading is insignificant if the internal resistance of the voltmeter is much higher than the resistance across which it is connected. When the breadboard voltmeter is used to measure the voltage dropped across the relatively low resistance, 470 Ω resistor, it has very little loading effect. The reading on the breadboard voltmeter should be about the same as that recorded in Figure E13-3 for the 7.5 V setting.

The voltage drop across 470 Ω resistor R6 is still about half of the source voltage, or 7.5 V. The internal resistance of the breadboard voltmeter in the 10 V range is unchanged, about 50 kΩ. When connected in parallel with R6, which is now 470 Ω, this has almost no effect on the total resistance. The calculated reduction is less than 5 Ω, and the reduction in the voltage across R6 is less than 0.04 V. This reduction is barely measurable, and is small enough to be able to ignore.

The last part of this exercise will give you a chance to observe the characteristics of an AC voltmeter.

Procedure Continued

18. Switch the Trainer power off. Remove the wires and components from the breadboard. Then build the breadboard AC voltmeter circuit shown in Figure E13-7. This voltmeter has an input range of 0 to 10V AC.

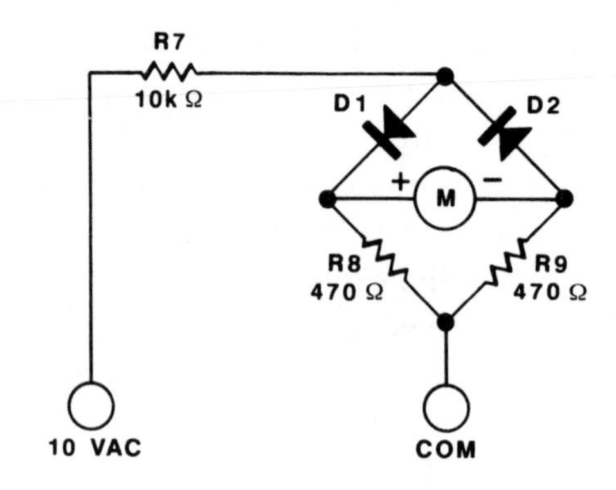

Figure E13-7
Simple AC voltmeter circuit.

19. Connect your breadboard AC voltmeter, along with an AC voltmeter, to the AC voltage divider circuit shown in Figure E13-8. Set pot R10 fully counterclockwise, for minimum voltage to the meters.

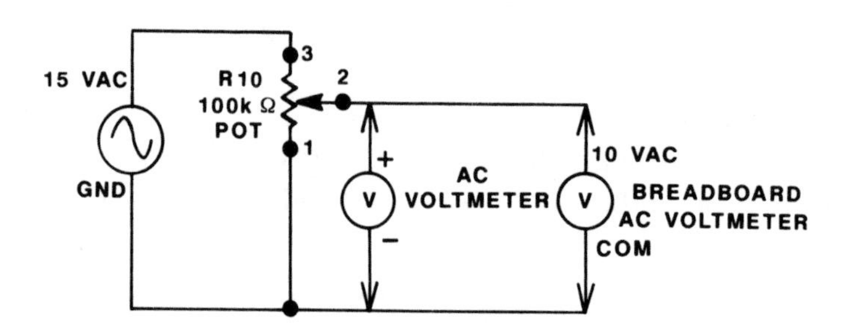

Figure E13-8
Circuit to test the breadboard AC voltmeter.

20. Switch the Trainer power on. Adjust pot R10 for a reading of 1 V on your AC voltmeter. Record the reading of you breadboard AC voltmeter in the "breadboard AC voltmeter voltage" column of Figure E13-9. Notice that this is just the opposite from what you did in previous meter tests. Continue to adjust the voltage with the pot and record the measured value for the remaining voltage values in Figure 13-9. When you finish, switch the Trainer power off.

BREADBOARD AC VOLTMETER VOLTAGE	MEASURED AC VOLTAGE
	1 V
	2 V
	3 V
	4 V
	5 V
	6 V
	7 V
	8 V
	9 V
	10 V

Figure E13-9
Chart of breadboard AC voltmeter characteristics.

21. Now use the information from the previous step to create a new scale for your breadboard AC voltmeter. Use the meter outline shown in Figure E13-10. We've add a second arc to the scale, to make it easier to add the appropriate scale divisions. A dot, near the bottom of the meter outline, indicates the center of rotation for the pointer. This allows you to use a ruler to mark the new lower scale divisions at the same angle as the old upper scale divisions. Use the data in Figure E13-9 to locate the position of each division and identify its value. For example, suppose

you recorded 0.3 in the breadboard AC voltmeter column for an actual value of 1 V. Lay your ruler from the dot to the position 0.3 on the upper scale and draw a short line on the lower scale. Label this division "1". Then do the same thing for the next value, and so on, until you have recorded all of the AC voltage values. To avoid clutter, you may wish to label only every other division on the scale, like the original scale is labeled. When you finish, you will have a scale that you can use to make relatively accurate readings with your breadboard AC voltmeter. Creating this new scale gets you around the problem of a non-linear meter movement.

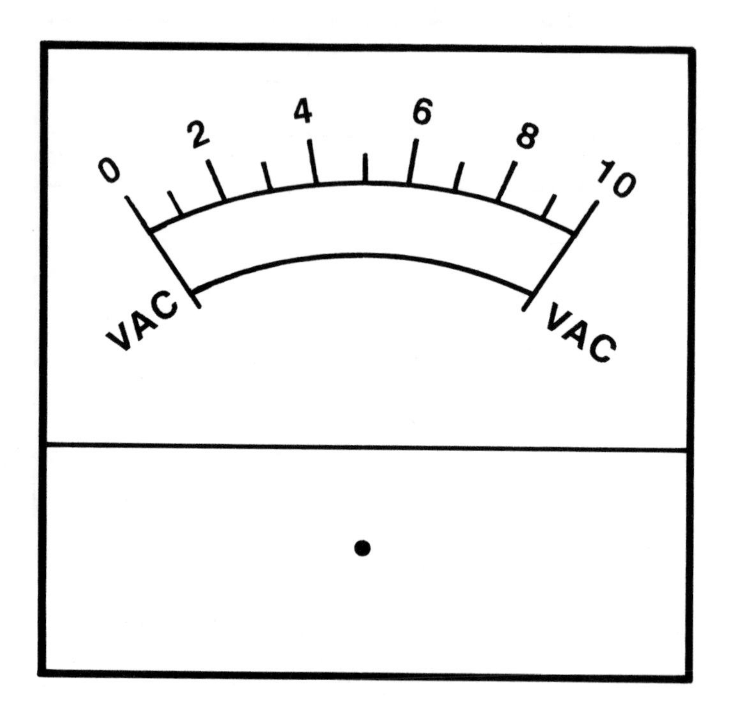

Figure E13-10

Meter scale.

22. To verify the accuracy of your new AC voltmeter scale, build the simple series AC circuit in Figure E13-11. Switch the Trainer power on and measure the voltage dropped across resistor R12. Using your new scale, your breadboard AC voltmeter reads ______V. Your AC voltmeter reads ______V. The calculated voltage drop across resistor R12 is ______. Switch the Trainer power off.

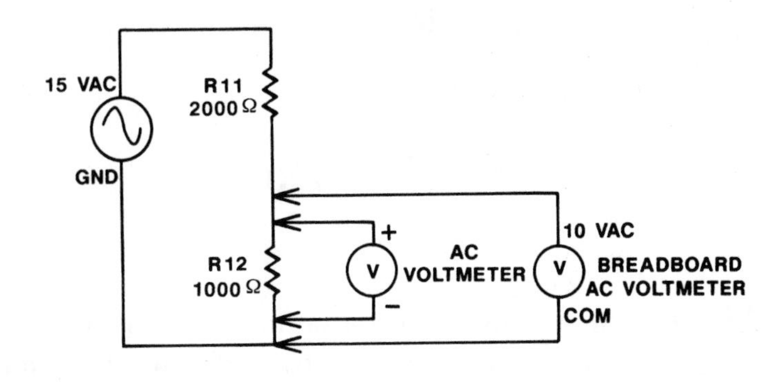

Figure E13-11
Simple series AC circuit.

Discussion

In addition to the basic non-linearity of the meter movement, the diode circuit in the AC voltmeter adds an additional amount of non-linearity to the display. Even so, it is still possible to use that moving-coil meter movement to make accurate measurements. You did this by constructing a meter scale that is calibrated to the AC meter circuit characteristics. Naturally, you had to assume that the instrument AC voltmeter you used is accurate. In actual practice, meter manufacturers use a very accurate voltage source, known as a "voltage standard," to calibrate the AC meter scale.

In the last circuit you built, the calculated voltage drop across resistor R12 is 5 V rms. The AC voltmeter and your breadboard AC voltmeter should have indicated 5 V rms. However, because of the 5% resistor tolerance in the circuit, you could see an error of ±0.25 V.

Procedure Continued

23. Remove the wire and components from the Trainer breadboard and save them for future exercises. Remember to short the terminals of the meter movement. Clean-up your work area.

24. This completes Exercise 13. Proceed to the next exercise, where you will study the ohmmeter.

EXERCISE 14

The Ohmmeter

PURPOSE: Show how to use a permanent-magnet moving-coil meter movement to construct a simple ohmmeter.

Show how to experimentally calibrate an ohmmeter.

Material Required

Trainer.
VOM or individual DC voltmeter and ohmmeter.
Meter movement, Heath #407-719.
1 100 Ω resistor.
1 270 Ω resistor.
1 470 Ω resistor.
1 820 Ω resistor.
1 1000 Ω resistor.
1 1500 Ω resistor.
1 2000 Ω resistor.
1 3830 Ω resistor.
1 4020 Ω resistor.
1 5600 Ω resistor.
1 6040 Ω resistor.
1 6800 Ω resistor.
1 10 kΩ resistor.
1 12 kΩ resistor.
1 15 kΩ resistor.
1 20 kΩ resistor.
1 27 kΩ resistor.
1 30 kΩ resistor.
1 40.2 kΩ resistor.
1 45.3 kΩ resistor.
1 100 kΩ resistor.
White #22 copper hook-up wire.

Introduction

The third electrical quantity that is easily measured with a permanent-magnet moving-coil meter movement is resistance. Simply add a few resistors and a power source to the meter movement, and you have an ohmmeter. In this exercise, you will build an ohmmeter and construct a resistance scale for your meter. Then, you will modify the circuit to add a scale with more resolution. Finally, you will test your breadboard ohmmeter by measuring the resistance of several resistors.

Procedure

1. Figure E14-1 shows the circuit diagram of a simple single-range ohmmeter. If the wiper of pot R1 is adjusted to the center of its range—500 Ω—and the meter circuit input terminals are shorted together, what value of resistor R2 will produce full-scale deflection of the meter pointer? ________Ω

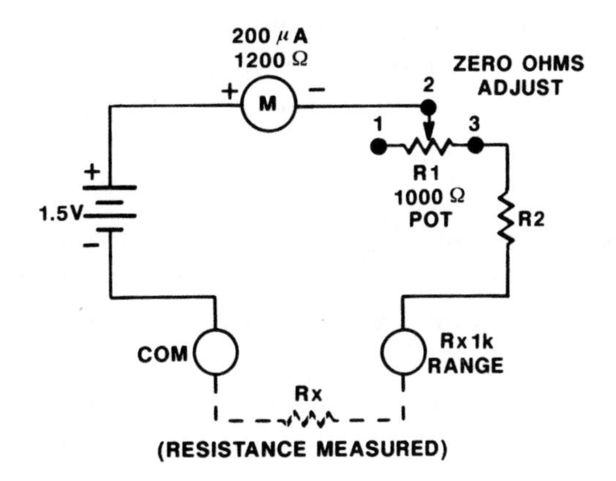

Figure E14-1
Simple ohmmeter circuit.

Discussion

In the single-range ohmmeter circuit of Figure E14-1, the full-scale current will flow when the external resistance is zero ohms—input terminals shorted together. You know that full-scale current equals 200 μA and the circuit has a 1.5 V power source. Therefore, it's a simple matter to calculate the total circuit resistance of 7500 Ω. Subtract the resistance of the meter and the pot, and you know the resistance of resistor R2 must equal 5800 Ω. Now a 5800 Ω resistor is not a standard off-the-shelf value. However, since you have a 1000 Ω pot in the circuit, you can select the nearest standard value, which is 5600 Ω. The pot allows you to adjust for the difference in resistor values, plus any variation in the resistance of the meter coil. The pot also allows you to adjust for small changes in the supply voltage — very important if you were using a battery for the power source.

Now that you know all the ohmmeter component values, you can build the ohmmeter circuit.

Procedure Continued

2. Switch the Trainer power on and adjust the positive DC voltage supply to 1.5 V. Switch the Trainer power off. Write the value 5600 Ω next to resistor R2, in Figure E14-1. Then build the circuit in the figure.

   To distinguish between this ohmmeter and your instrument ohmmeter, we will call this circuit your "breadboard ohmmeter," and your instrument ohmmeter, simply an "ohmmeter."

3. Switch the Trainer power on. Zero your breadboard ohmmeter by shorting the input terminals together and adjusting pot R1 until you obtain exactly full-scale deflection on the meter movement. When the meter is "zeroed," remove the shorting wire from the input.

   Now that you have a working ohmmeter, you need to calibrate the meter scale. You will do this in the next set step by connecting different value resistors to the input terminals and recording the meter pointer position on the blank meter scale in Figure E14-2.

Be sure to mark the scale divisions like you did for the AC voltmeter scale in the previous exercise. This time, though, label each division with the "test resistor" value, in thousands of ohms. That is, 1000 Ω is marked "1", 30 kΩ is marked "30", etc.

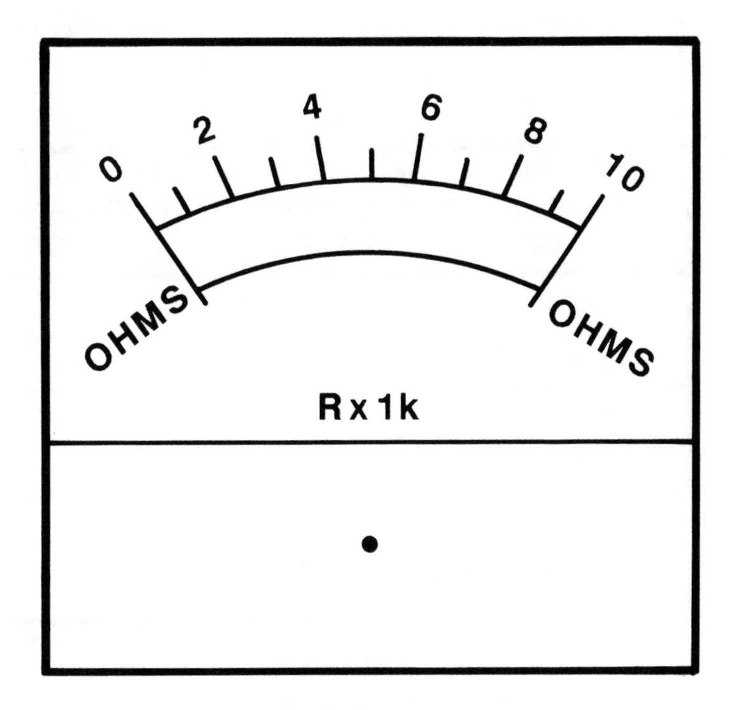

Figure E14-2

Meter scale.

4. Locate the following resistors. Then one-by-one, connect each resistor to the input terminals of your breadboard ohmmeter and record its value in Figure E14-2. Be sure to also mark the scale with the zero (full-scale deflection) and infinite (no deflection) ohms symbols to make the scale complete.

   1000 Ω
   2000 Ω
   4020 Ω
   6040 Ω
   10 kΩ
   15 kΩ
   20 kΩ
   30 kΩ
   40.2 kΩ
   100 kΩ

5. Now that you have a working and calibrated ohmmeter, it's time to compare its performance with your instrument ohmmeter. Locate the resistors listed in Figure E14-3. Measure each resistor using your breadboard ohmmeter and calibrated meter scale, and record the value in the appropriate column. Then measure and record the value for each resistor, one more time, using the instrument ohmmeter. When you are finished, switch the Trainer power off.

NOMINAL RESISTOR VALUE	BREADBOARD OHMMETER READING	MEASURED RESISTANCE VALUE
1500 Ω		
3830 Ω		
6800 Ω		
12 kΩ		
27 kΩ		
45.3 kΩ		

Figure E14-3
Chart to evaluate the performance of the breadboard ohmmeter.

Discussion

The values of resistance we had you use for meter calibration were selected to place a division at somewhat evenly spaced intervals on the scale. The actual locations will depend on the characteristics of your particular meter movement and the tolerance error of the resistors.

Since you have now calibrated your meter, you should be able to use your new scale and read resistances fairly accurately. You used 5% resistors for most of the calibration, so the values may be in error by that much. The non-linearity of you meter between calibration marks will also affect your measurements to some degree. And finally, the tolerance of the resistors in Figure E14-3 will also affect your readings. If you are in error by more than 10%, go back and check your calibration. You may have bumped your "zero" adjust pot, or the power supply control.

In the next section, you will change the breadboard ohmmeter circuit to make an R × 100 range ohmmeter.

Procedure Continued

6. Refer to Figure E14-4. What is the value of the new R × 100 range shunt resistor, R3? ________Ω

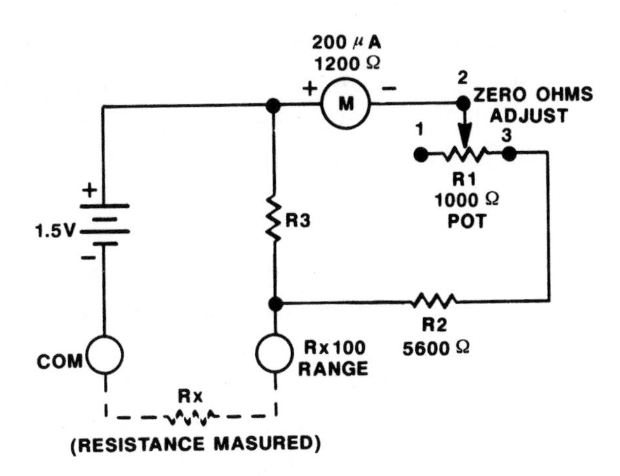

Figure E14-4
Ohmmeter circuit for R × 100 range.

Discussion

Did you remember how to make the calculation? Shunt resistor R3 is used to decrease the sensitivity of the meter circuit by a factor of 10. In order to calculate the value of R3, you need to know the other two electrical quantities for R3: the voltage and the current. As you discovered, the process for determining these values requires some imagination and several calculations.

When you calculated the value of resistor R2 in Figure E14-1, you assumed the external resistance, Rx, was zero—the test leads were shorted together. This, however, is not a practical method to calculate the value of R3. It's much easier if you work with the assumption that the meter movement current is 50% of full-scale. Here's the process.

Begin with the single-range ohmmeter circuit in Figure E14-1 and calculate the value of external resistance, Rx, that will cause 50% of full-scale current to flow in the circuit. To arrive at that value, you calculate the total circuit resistance—the sum of the internal and external resistances—and then subtract the internal resistance. Now you know that half-scale current equals 100 μA, and the source voltage is 1.5 V. Therefore, the total circuit resistance for an ohmmeter with half-scale deflection is 15 kΩ. You also know the internal breadboard ohmmeter resistance is 7500 Therefore, the value of Rx is the difference between the total circuit resistance and the internal circuit resistance, or 7500 Ω.

You've determined that an external resistance of 7500 Ω will cause half-scale deflection on the R × 1K ohmmeter range. Therefore, the external resistance that will cause half-scale deflection on the R × 100 range of the ohmmeter in Figure E14-4 must be one-tenth of that value, or 750 Ω.

Now, if you let Rx, in Figure E14-4, equal 750 Ω, and assume the meter movement current is 50% of full-scale, you can calculate the value of R3. You know from previous calculations that the resistance of the branch of the circuit containing the meter coil in series with resistors R1 and R2 is 7500 Ω. In addition, you know that 50% full-scale current, or 100 μA, flowing through this branch of the circuit will produce a branch voltage drop of 0.75 V. Since resistor R3 is in parallel with the meter movement branch, the voltage drop across R3 is 0.75 V. With a source voltage of 1.5 V, the voltage drop across external resistor Rx must be 0.75 V. Knowing the voltage across Rx, you can calculate its current to be 1 mA, 1000 μA. This is the total current from the source, which divides between R3 and the meter branch of the parallel circuit. With 100 μA of current in the meter branch, the current through R3 must equal 900 μA. At last, you know the current through R3 and the voltage dropped across R3 and you can calculate the resistance of R3 to equal 833 Ω.

Since an 833 Ω resistor is not a standard off-the-shelf value, you must substitute a value that is. You'll find an 820 Ω resistor in the parts pack that will work quite well, since it is within 2% of the calculated value.

Procedure Continued

7. Refer to Figure E14-4 and write the value 820 Ω next to resistor R3. Then add resistor R3 to your breadboard ohmmeter circuit as shown in Figure E14-4. Switch the Trainer power on and zero the breadboard ohmmeter. Locate the resistors listed in Figure E14-5. Measure each resistor using your breadboard ohmmeter and calibrated meter scale, and record the value in the appropriate column. Remember that you are now using R × 100 range on the breadboard ohmmeter, so you must multiply the meter scale value by 100 rather than by 1000, to determine the correct resistance value. Then measure and record the value for each resistor, one more time, using the instrument ohmmeter. When you are finished, switch the Trainer power off.

NOMINAL RESISTOR VALUE	BREADBOARD OHMMETER READING	MEASURED RESISTANCE VALUE
100 Ω		
270 Ω		
470 Ω		
1000 Ω		
2000 Ω		
6040 Ω		

Figure E14-5

Chart to evaluate the performance of the R × 100 range.

Discussion

When you adjust the new ohmmeter range for zero ohms, you shouldn't have to change the pot setting very much. If you have to make a large change in the pot setting, go back and check your circuit connections, resistor values, and source voltage setting.

Because you changed the range of your breadboard ohmmeter by a factor of ten, the meter calibration should not have changed. Therefore, you should have observed the same measurement characteristics as before.

Procedure Continued

8. This completes Exercise 14 and the exercises for Unit 6. Remove the wire and components from the Trainer, and save them for future exercises. Remember to short the terminals of the meter movement and put it in a safe place. Put away your equipment and clean-up your work area.

9. Return to Unit 6 and complete the Unit Examination.

UNIT 1 EXAMINATION

Direct Current

1. Which of the following is a definition of current?

   A. The potential, or force that moves electrons.
   B. Work over time.
   C. The movement of electrons through a material.
   D. The reduction or control of current flow.

2. What part of an atom contains a negative charge?

   A. Nucleus.
   B. Electron.
   C. Proton.
   D. Neutron.

3. What is a source of many free electrons?

   A. Resistor.
   B. Insulator.
   C. Conductor.
   D. Nonconductor.

4. Which of the meters in Figure U1-1 is measuring current, voltage, or resistance?

   A. The ammeter is measuring current.
   B. The voltmeter is measuring voltage.
   C. The ohmmeter is measuring resistance.
   D. All of the above.

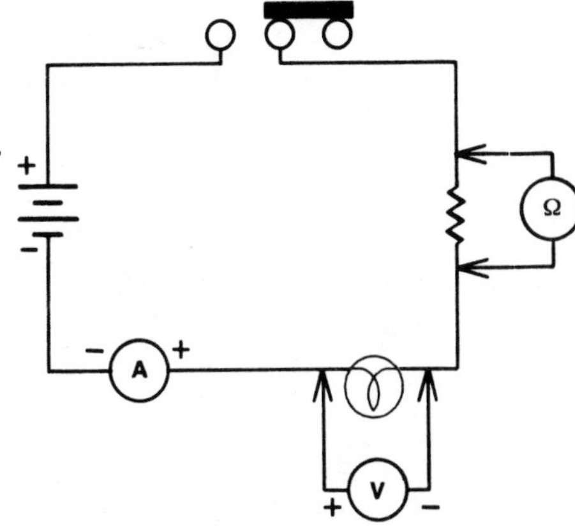

Figure U1-1
Figure for questions 4 and 5.

5. Which of the meters in Figure U1-1 is **not** correctly connected to the circuit?

   A. The ammeter.
   B. The voltmeter.
   C. The ohmmeter.
   D. None of the above.

6. What is the unit of measure for current?

   A. Watt.
   B. Ohm.
   C. Volt.
   D. Amp.

7. A heater that is designed to operate at 120 volts has a nichrome wire heating element that is 15 feet long. If the nichrome wire has a resistance of 250 ohms-per-foot, how much current will flow through the heater?

   A. 32 A
   B. 3.2 A
   C. 320 mA
   D. 32 mA

8. Which of the following is a definition of voltage?

   A. The potential, or force that moves electrons.
   B. Work over time.
   C. The movement of electrons through a material.
   D. The reduction or control of current flow.

9. What is the unit of measure for voltage?

   A. Watt.
   B. Ohm.
   C. Volt.
   D. Amp.

10. You measure a potential difference of 6 volts across a resistor in an electrical circuit. What is another term for this potential difference?

    A. Voltage transition.
    B. Voltage peak.
    C. Voltage rise.
    D. Voltage drop.

11. If the power supply in Figure U1-1 has a voltage of 12 volts, the lamp has a resistance of 100 ohms, and the resistor has a resistance of 50 ohms, how much voltage is dropped across the resistor?

    A. Zero volts.
    B. Four volts.
    C. Eight volts.
    D. All the voltage, because the switch is open.

12. Which of the following is a definition of resistance?

    A. The potential, or force that moves electrons.
    B. Work over time.
    C. The movement of electrons through a material.
    D. The reduction or control of current flow.

13. What is the unit of measure for resistance?

    A. Watt.
    B. Ohm.
    C. Volt.
    D. Amp.

14. Which of the following is **not** considered a resistor?

    A. Glass.
    B. Lamp filament.
    C. Nichrome wire.
    D. Carbon.

15. If the current through a circuit is 10 amps, and the voltage dropped across a resistor in the circuit is 10 volts, what is the value of the resistor?

    A. 100 ohms.
    B. 10 ohms.
    C. 1 ohm.
    D. 0.1 ohm.

16. Which of the following is stated in Ohm's Law?

    A. Voltage and current are inversely proportional.
    B. Resistance and current are directly proportional.
    C. Voltage and current are directly proportional.
    D. Resistance and voltage are inversely proportional.

17. A circuit contains two resistors and a power supply. If the first resistor drops 10 volts, the second resistor has a resistance of 80 ohms, and there is 0.1 amps flowing through the circuit, what is the power supply voltage?

    A. 2 volts.
    B. 10.8 volts
    C. 18 volts
    D. 90 volts

18. Which of the following is a definition of power?

    A. The potential, or force that moves electrons.
    B. Work over time.
    C. The movement of electrons through a material.
    D. The reduction or control of current flow.

19. What is the unit of measure for power?

    A. Watt.
    B. Ohm.
    C. Volt.
    D. Amp.

20. A heater that is designed to operate at 120 volts has a nichrome wire heating element that is 15 feet long. If the nichrome wire has a resistance of 250 ohms-per-foot, how much power is dissipated by the heater?

A. 3840 watts.
B. 384 watts.
C. 38.4 watts.
D. 3.84 watts.

UNIT 2 EXAMINATION

Circuit Theory

1. Which of the schematics in Figure U2-1 illustrates a series circuit?

   A. Part A.
   B. Part B.
   C. Part C.
   D. Part B and C.

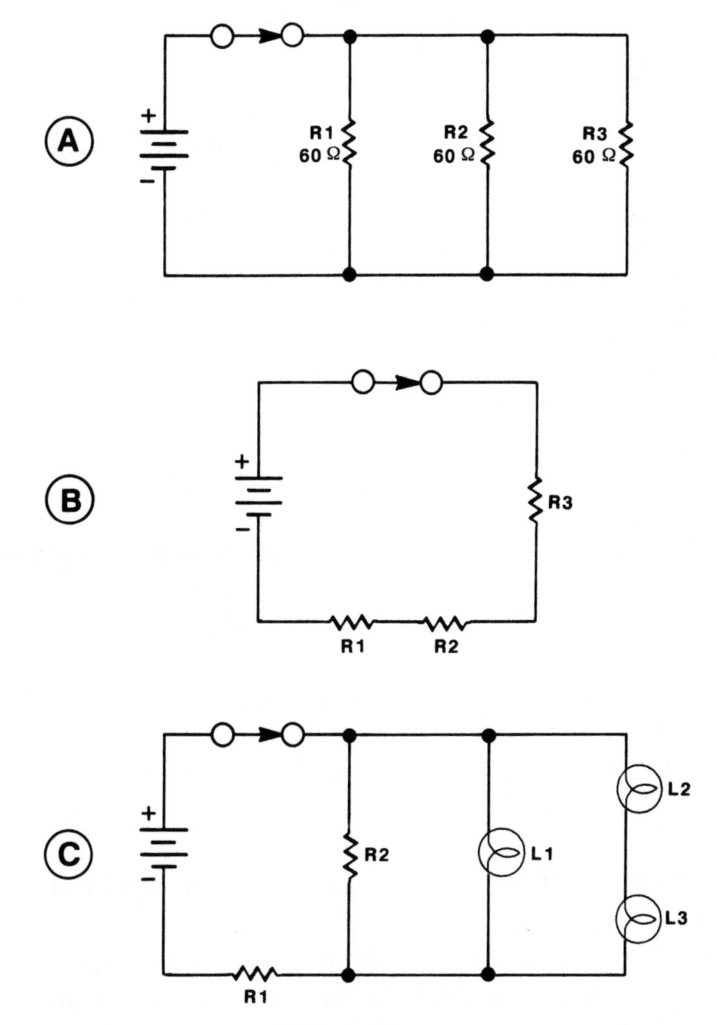

Figure U2-1
Figure for questions 1 through 3.

2. Which of the schematics in Figure U2-1 illustrates a parallel circuit?

   A. Part A.
   B. Part B.
   C. Part C.
   D. Part A and C.

3. Which of the schematics in Figure U2-1 illustrates a series-parallel circuit?

   A. Part A.
   B. Part B.
   C. Part C.
   D. All of the schematics in the figure.

4. Which of the following is true of a series circuit?

   A. Current is constant and the sum of the voltage drops equals the voltage rise.
   B. Voltage is constant and the sum of the branch currents equals the source current.
   C. Resistance is constant and the sum of the voltage drops equals the voltage rise.
   D. Power is constant and the sum of the voltage drops equals the voltage rise.

5. Which of the following is true of a parallel circuit?

   A. Current is constant and the sum of the voltage drops equals the voltage rise.
   B. Voltage is constant and the sum of the branch currents equals the source current.
   C. Resistance is constant and the sum of the voltage drops equals the voltage rise.
   D. Power is constant and the sum of the voltage drops equals the voltage rise.

6. Which of the following is true of a series-parallel circuit?

   A. The sum of the voltage drops equals the voltage rise.
   B. The sum of the branch and series currents equals the source current.
   C. The sum of the individual resistances is equal to the total resistance.
   D. The sum of the power consumed by the individual components is equal to the total power consumed.

7. If a series circuit contains two equal-value resistors, its total current is 15 milliamps, and its voltage rise is 15 volts, what is the value of each resistor?

   A. 100 Ω
   B. 500 Ω
   C. 1000 Ω
   D. 2000 Ω

8. If a parallel circuit contains two equal-value resistors, its total current is 15 milliamps, and its voltage rise is 15 volts, what is the value of each resistor?

   A. 100 Ω
   B. 500 Ω
   C. 1000 Ω
   D. 2000 Ω

9. Which of the following statements is true of the equal-branch method of determining resistance in a 2-resistor parallel circuit?

   A. Total resistance is equal to the product of the branch resistances divided by the sum of the branch resistances.
   B. Total resistance is equal to the sum of the branch resistances divided by branch resistance.
   C. Total resistance is equal to the sum of the branch resistances divided by the product of the branch resistances.
   D. Total resistance is equal to the branch resistance divided by the number of branches.

10. Which of the following statements is true of the product-over-the-sum method of determining resistance in a 2-resistor parallel circuit?

   A. Total resistance is equal to the product of the branch resistances divided by the sum of the branch resistances.
   B. Total resistance is equal to the sum of the branch resistances divided by branch resistance.
   C. Total resistance is equal to the sum of the branch resistances divided by the product of the branch resistances.
   D. Total resistance is equal to the branch resistance divided by the number of branches.

11. What is the resistance of resistor R3 in Figure U2-2?

A. 50 Ω
B. 100 Ω
C. 150 Ω
D. 200 Ω

12. What is the resistance of resistor R1 in Figure U2-2?

A. 50 Ω
B. 75 Ω
C. 100 Ω
D. 150 Ω

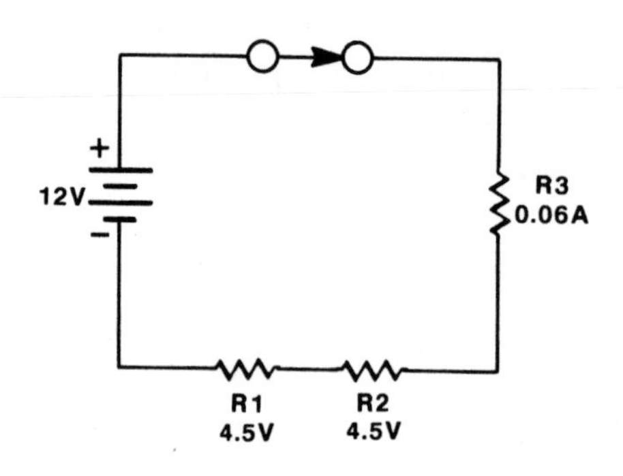

Figure U2-2
Figure for questions 11 and 12.

13. What is the total resistance of the circuit in Figure U2-3?

A. 120 Ω
B. 90 Ω
C. 40 Ω
D. 36 Ω

14. What is the total current in the circuit in Figure U2-3?

A. 0.05 A
B. 0.15 A
C. 0.3 A
D. 0.5 A

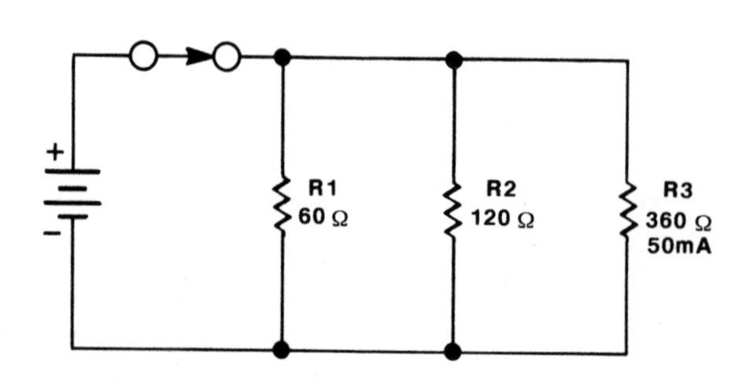

Figure U2-3
Figure for questions 13 and 14.

15. What is the total resistance of the circuit in Figure U2-4?

A. 240 Ω
B. 60 Ω
C. 15 Ω
D. 6 Ω

16. Assuming you wish to use the smallest resistor possible in the circuit in Figure U2-4, what wattage would you select for resistor R1?

A. 1/8-watt
B. 1/4-watt
C. 1/2-watt
D. 1-watt

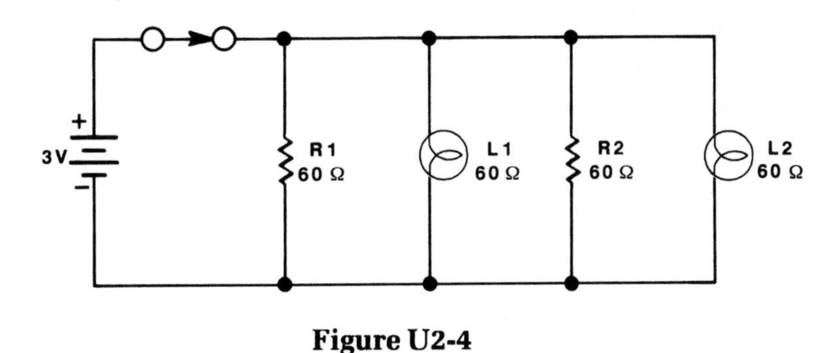

Figure U2-4
Figure for questions 15 and 16.

17. What is the current through lamp L2 in Figure U2-5?

A. 45 mA
B. 30 mA
C. 15 mA
D. 7.5 mA

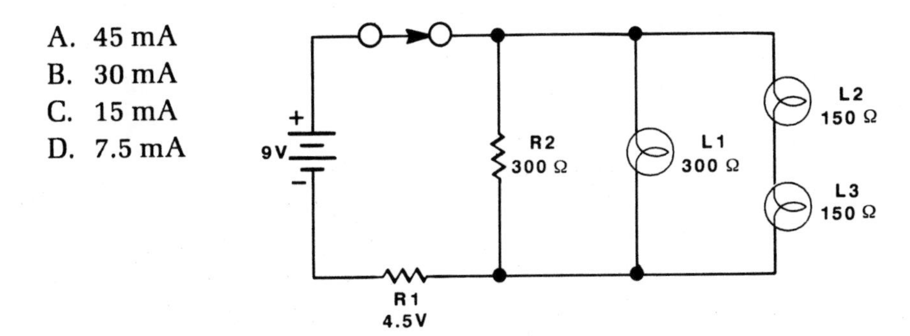

Figure U2-5
Figure for questions 17 through 20.

18. What is the resistance of resistor R1 in Figure U2-5?

A. 50 Ω
B. 100 Ω
C. 150 Ω
D. 300 Ω

19. What is the current through resistor R1 in Figure U2-5?

A. 45 mA
B. 30 mA
C. 15 mA
D. 7.5 mA

20. What is the power consumption of all three lamps in Figure U2-5?

A. 0.0675 W
B. 0.135 W
C. 0.2025 W
D. 0.405 W

UNIT 3 EXAMINATION

Electromechanical Systems

1. Which of the following is a naturally formed magnet?

   A. A compass needle.
   B. Lodestone.
   C. Mica.
   D. A pole shoe.

2. What determines the magnetic properties of a bar of steel?

   A. Its molecules.
   B. Its shape.
   C. Its insulation.
   D. Its conductivity.

3. What can be said of the magnetic flux in a permanent magnet?

   A. It is more concentrated at the south pole than at the north pole.
   B. It is more concentrated at the north pole than at the south pole.
   C. It flows out of the south pole and into the north pole of the magnet.
   D. It flows out of the north pole and into the south pole of the magnet.

4. Which of the following terms is used to describe the process where a magnetic field is used to magnetically align the molecules in an iron object?

   A. Conduction.
   B. Reduction.
   C. Induction.
   D. Subjunction.

5. What does the "left-hand magnetic-field rule" state?

   A. Your fingers point in the direction of current flow.
   B. Your thumb points in the direction of current flow.
   C. Your thumb points toward the south pole.
   D. Your fingers point toward the north pole.

6. Which of the following statements is true?

   A. The magnetic field around a straight conductor has a north and a south pole.
   B. If the lines of flux for two parallel conductors are rotating in the same direction, the conductors are repelled from each other.
   C. If the lines of flux for two parallel conductors are rotating in opposite directions, the conductors are repelled from each other.
   D. A magnetic field must have a north and a south pole.

7. What does the "left-hand rule for coils" state?

   A. Your fingers point in the direction of current flow.
   B. Your thumb points in the direction of current flow.
   C. Your thumb points toward the south pole.
   D. Your fingers point toward the north pole.

8. If an electromagnet has a coil with 200 turns of wire and it consumes 500 milliamps of current, what is its ampere-turns rating?

   A. 1000.
   B. 100.
   C. 10.
   D. 1.

9. What is the purpose of a solenoid?

   A. Convert electrical energy into magnetic energy.
   B. Convert electrical energy into rotary motion.
   C. Convert electrical energy into linear motion.
   D. Control a large current with a small current.

10. What are the two basic parts that make up a solenoid?

    A. The armature and the plunger.
    B. The coil and the armature.
    C. The frame and the coil.
    D. The coil and the plunger.

11. What is the purpose of a relay?

    A. Convert electrical energy into magnetic energy.
    B. Convert electrical energy into rotary motion.
    C. Convert electrical energy into linear motion.
    D. Control a large current with a small current.

Refer to Figure U3-1 for the next six questions. Match the questions with the letters in figure.

12. Coil ______

13. Armature ______

14. N.O. contact ______

15. N.C. contact ______

16. Moving contact ______

17. Spring ______

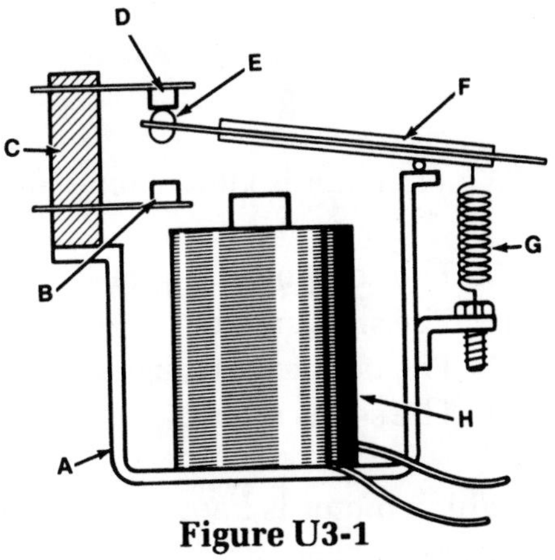

Figure U3-1
Figure for questions 12 through 18.

18. What kind of relay is shown in Figure U3-1?

    A. Double-contact relay.
    B. Permanent magnet relay.
    C. Normally closed relay.
    D. Normally open relay.

19. What is the purpose of a motor?

    A. Convert electrical energy into magnetic energy.
    B. Convert electrical energy into rotary motion.
    C. Convert electrical energy into linear motion.
    D. Control a large current with a small current.

20. What motor assembly is shown in Figure U3-2?

A. Pole shoe.
B. Brush assembly.
C. Field windings.
D. Armature.

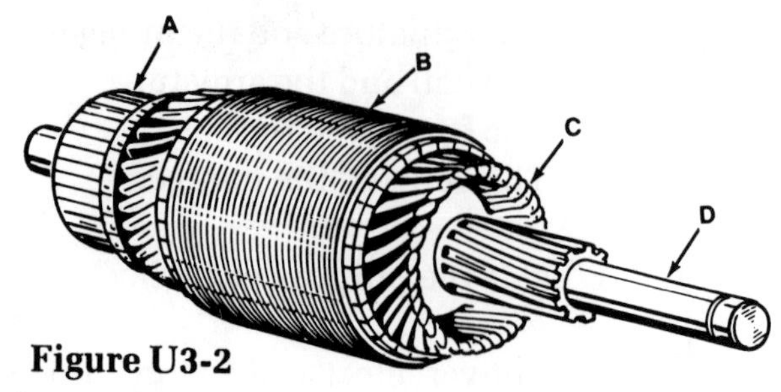

Figure U3-2
Figure for questions 20 and 21.

21. Which letter in Figure U3-2 identifies the commutator?

A. A.
B. B.
C. C.
D. D.

22. Which motor is known for a high starting torque?

A. The compound motor.
B. The shunt motor.
C. The permanent magnet motor.
D. The series motor.

23. Which motor is known for a good starting torque and speed regulation.

A. The compound motor.
B. The shunt motor.
C. The permanent magnet motor.
D. The series motor.

24. Which motor is known for a low starting torque but excellent speed regulation?

A. The compound motor.
B. The shunt motor.
C. The permanent magnet motor.
D. The series motor.

25. Which motor often used in low-power, battery operated toys?

A. The compound motor.
B. The shunt motor.
C. The permanent magnet motor.
D. The series motor.

UNIT 4 EXAMINATION

Alternating Current

1. Which of the following describes the waveform in Figure U4-1?

   A. A DC waveform, because it doesn't have a sinusoidal shape.
   B. An AC waveform, because it has a sinusoidal shape.
   C. A DC waveform, because it never changes polarity.
   D. An AC waveform, because its amplitude varies.

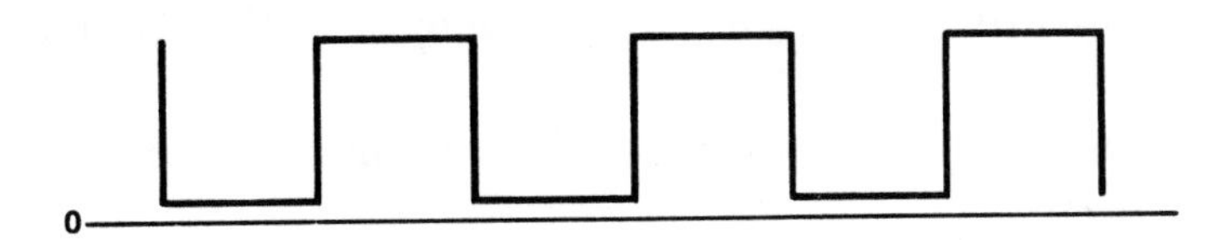

Figure U4-1
Figure for question 1.

2. Alternating current is measured in units of:

   A. Volts.
   B. Amperes.
   C. Potential difference.
   D. Ohms.

3. What does Ohm's Law state for AC?

   A. AC current increases as resistance increases.
   B. AC current decreases as AC voltage increases.
   C. AC current increases as AC voltage increases.
   D. Resistance increases as AC voltage decreases.

4. Which of the following equations expresses Ohm's Law for AC?

A. $I = \frac{E}{R}$

B. $I = E \times R$

C. $R = E \times I$

D. $E = \frac{R}{I}$

5. If a simple AC circuit with a 120-volt source has 2.4 amps of current flowing through it, what is the circuit resistance?

A. 0.02 Ω
B. 50 Ω
C. 288 Ω
D. Insufficient information given to solve the problem.

6. Household AC uses the most common waveform. What is it called?

A. Sawtooth wave.
B. Sine wave.
C. Triangle wave.
D. Square wave.

7. One complete cycle of an AC sine wave contains:

A. Two positive alternations and one negative alternation.
B. Two negative alternations.
C. Only one alternation.
D. One positive alternation and one negative alternation.

8. What is the maximum value that occurs during the sine wave cycle called?

A. Point of the sine wave.
B. Peak-to-peak value.
C. Peak value.
D. Positive peak-to-peak value.

9. A sine wave has a peak value of 200 volts. What is its average value?

   A. 127 V.
   B. 141 V.
   C. 283 V.
   D. 314 V.

10. What is the effective or rms value of a sine wave with a peak-to-peak value of 32 amps?

    A. 10.2 A.
    B. 11.3 A.
    C. 20.4 A.
    D. 22.6 A.

11. In what value are most AC voltmeters and ammeters calibrated to measure?

    A. Effective or rms.
    B. Average.
    C. Peak.
    D. Peak-to-peak.

12. What value of AC current will do the same amount of work as 1 amp of constant DC?

    A. 1 A peak.
    B. 1 A peak-to-peak.
    C. 1 A average.
    D. 1 A rms or effective.

13. What values must you use to calculate power in an AC circuit?

    A. The average values for voltage and current.
    B. The average value for current and the rms value for voltage.
    C. The rms values for both current and voltage.
    D. The peak-to-peak value for current and the rms value for voltage.

14. What is the equation for calculating AC power?

A. $P = I \times E$
B. $P = R \times E$
C. $P = \frac{E}{I}$
D. $P = I \times R$

15. If a 120-volt AC source is connected to a 1000-ohm resistor, how much power will the resistor dissipate?

A. 0.12 W
B. 8.33 W
C. 14.4 W
D. 120,000 W

16. How many kilowatt-hours of electric energy will be used if I leave a 7-watt night light on for one month (30 days)?

A. 4.29 kWh
B. 5.04 kWh
C. 210 kWh
D. 5040 kWh

17. What is the total circuit current for the circuit of Figure U4-2?

A. 0.50 A
B. 0.75 A
C. 1.33 A
D. 3.20 A

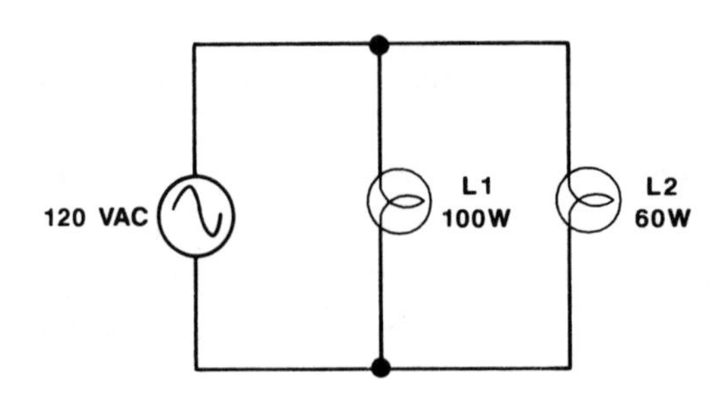

Figure U4-2
Figure for question 17.

18. Refer to Figure U4-3. What is the voltage drop across R1?

A. 57.3 V peak.
B. 81 V peak.
C. 99 V peak-to-peak.
D. 270 V peak-to-peak.

19. In Figure U4-3, what is the total circuit current?

A. 0.30 A.
B. 0.42 A peak-to-peak.
C. 0.60 A peak.
D. 1.67 A peak.

20. What is the the power dissipated in R3 in Figure U4-3?

A. 4.5 W
B. 9.0 W
C. 27 W
D. 30 W

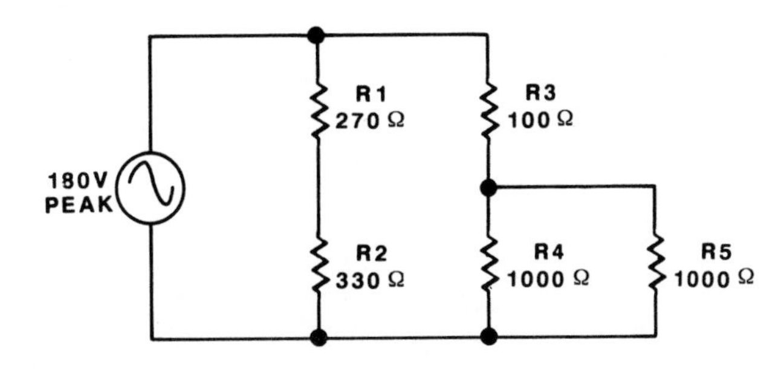

Figure U4-3
Figure for questions 18 through 20.

UNIT 5 EXAMINATION

Generators And Motors

1. What is magnetic induction?

   A. A magnetic field is created around a conductor by passing a current through the conductor.
   B. A current is induced in a conductor by a moving magnetic field.
   C. A magnetic field is created around a permanent magnet.
   D. Soft iron becomes magnetic when in contact with a permanent magnet.

2. What are the three ingredients needed for magnetic induction?

   A. Current, a magnetic field, and motion.
   B. A magnetic field, motion, and a conductor.
   C. A magnetic field, current, and a conductor.
   D. Current, motion, and a conductor.

3. How can you increase the induced current in a conductor?

   A. Increase the strength of the magnetic field.
   B. Increase the number of coils in the conductor.
   C. Increase the speed of motion.
   D. All of the above will cause an increase.

4. What is the primary advantage of the AC generator over the DC generator?

   A. An AC generator relies on commutator action to conduct the load current from its rotor.
   B. The DC generator induces load current to flow in its non-rotating stator.
   C. The shaft bearings of a DC generator are not as good as those in an AC generator.
   D. The AC generator induces load current to flow in its non-rotating stator.

5. Why is a capacitor is used with a generator?

   A. To convert AC to DC.
   B. To adjust the phase of the output current.
   C. To smooth out the current pulses.
   D. To increase the load current.

6. Describe a diode.

   A. It is a device that stores an electric charge.
   B. It is a device that allows electric current to pass in only one direction.
   C. It is a device that generates DC current.
   D. It is a device that filters AC current.

7. How does a capacitor filter the output of a rectifier?

   A. It cuts off the current peaks.
   B. It stores electrons.
   C. It converts AC to DC.
   D. It stores and then releases electrons.

8. What does a diode do?

   A. It converts AC to DC.
   B. It induces a DC current in a conductor.
   C. It creates a magnetic field around a conductor.
   D. It allows current to pass in four directions.

9. What is an alternator?

   A. It is a DC generator whose output is converted to AC.
   B. It is a DC series generator.
   C. It is an AC generator whose output is converted to DC.
   D. It is a generator that has a commutator.

10. How is the rotating magnetic field in a shaded-pole motor created?

    A. By spinning the field coil.
    B. With out-of-phase alternating magnetic fields.
    C. With two field coils with out-of-phase currents flowing in them.
    D. By inducing a current in the rotor.

11. In transformer action, what provides the motion required to induce a current?

    A. The vibration of the primary coil.
    B. The phase difference between primary and secondary current.
    C. A direct current in the secondary.
    D. The alternate expansion and collapse of the magnetic field from the primary coil.

12. How can you tell if two waveforms are in-phase?

    A. Both are current waveforms and have equal amplitude.
    B. Both cross zero together and always have the same polarity.
    C. Both are voltage waveforms of the same frequency.
    D. One is a current and the other is a voltage and they have the same frequency.

13. How fast does the rotor in a synchronous clock motor turn?

    A. 60 rpm.
    B. At slightly slower speed than the rotating magnetic field in the stator.
    C. The same speed as the rotating magnetic field in the stator.
    D. 3600 revolutions per second.

14. Which of the following is true about the rotor current in an induction motor?

    A. It is created by transformer action.
    B. It is created by induction due to the rotation of the rotor.
    C. Both A and B are correct.
    D. Neither A nor B is correct.

15. How does the starting coil of a split-phase induction motor cause a rotating magnetic field?

    A. Through transformer action.
    B. By inducing a current in the rotor.
    C. Through in-phase currents flowing in the starting and running windings.
    D. Through out-of-phase currents flowing in the starting and running windings.

16. What is the advantage of the shaded-pole motor and the induction motor over other motors?

    A. There are no electrical connections to the rotor.
    B. They run on AC power.
    C. They will run on AC or DC power.
    D. No current flows in the rotor.

17. What can you say about the rotor in an induction motor?

    A. It turns faster than the rotating magnetic field in the stator.
    B. It turns the same speed as the rotating magnetic field in the stator.
    C. It may turn the same speed or slower than the rotating magnetic field in the stator.
    D. It always turns slower than the rotating magnetic field in the stator.

18. Which of the following is true of a universal motor?

    A. It uses induction to turn the rotor.
    B. It operates on either AC or DC power.
    C. It runs best on DC power.
    D. It has poor starting torque.

19. Generally, where is the universal motor used?

    A. In small appliances such as hand drills.
    B. In industrial applications only.
    C. In any application where a motor is needed.
    D. In toys.

20. Why are AC motors, rather than DC motors, used most often in home and industry?

    A. A DC motor requires a battery.
    B. DC motors are more trouble-free than AC motors.
    C. AC motors use commutators.
    D. AC power is more commonly available than DC power.

UNIT 6 EXAMINATION

Meters

1. How is the d'Arsonval meter movement characterized?

   A. A moving coil that rotates in the field of a permanent magnet.
   B. A permanent magnet that rotates in the field of an electromagnet.
   C. A moving coil that rotates in the field of an electromagnet.
   D. A permanent magnet that rotates in the field of a stationary coil.

2. What typical schematic diagram does Figure U6-1 represent?

   A. Multirange DC voltmeter circuit.
   B. AC voltmeter circuit.
   C. Multirange DC milliammeter circuit.
   D. Ohmmeter circuit.

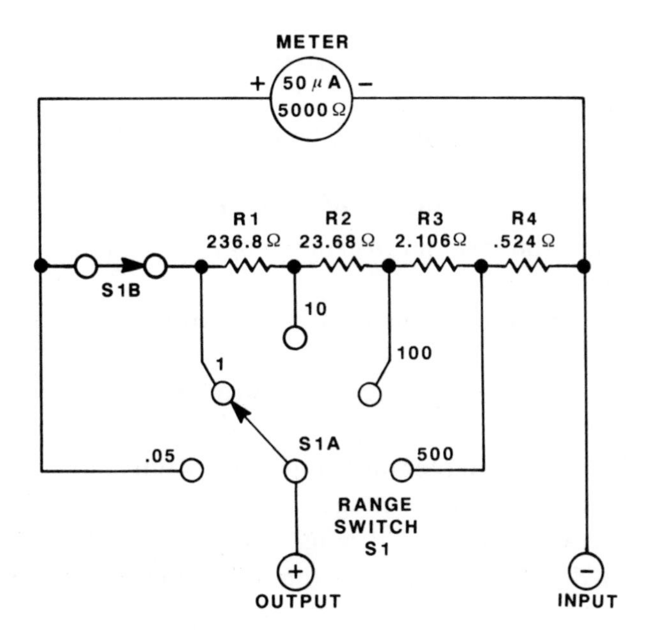

Figure U6-1
Figure for question 2.

3. How is the full-scale range of an ammeter increased?

   A. Switching a higher rated meter movement into the ammeter circuit.
   B. Placing a multiplier resistor in series with the meter movement.
   C. Placing a shunt resistor in parallel with the meter movement.
   D. Using a higher voltage battery in the ammeter circuit.

4. How is the full-scale range of a voltmeter increased?

   A. Placing a higher value multiplier resistor in series with the meter movement.
   B. Placing a lower value multiplier resistor in parallel with the meter movement.
   C. Using a higher value shunt resistor.
   D. Placing a lower value resistor in series with the meter movement.

5. The accuracy of an analog ammeter or voltmeter is specified as a percentage of error at some specific point. What is that point?

   A. Zero-scale deflection.
   B. Full-scale deflection.
   C. Quarter-scale deflection.
   D. Mid-scale deflection.

6. What can you do to minimize the loading effect of a voltmeter?

   A. Lower the internal resistance of the voltmeter as much as possible.
   B. Adjust the sensitivity of the voltmeter to 1000 ohms/volt.
   C. Raise the internal resistance of the voltmeter as high as possible.
   D. Connect the voltmeter in series rather than in parallel.

7. Why are diodes used in an AC voltmeter?

   A. To increase meter movement sensitivity.
   B. To block any DC voltages.
   C. To extend the useful range of the meter.
   D. To direct the flow of current through the meter movement.

8. Which meter scale in Figure U6-2 is used when measuring DC current?

A. A.
B. B.
C. C.
D. D.

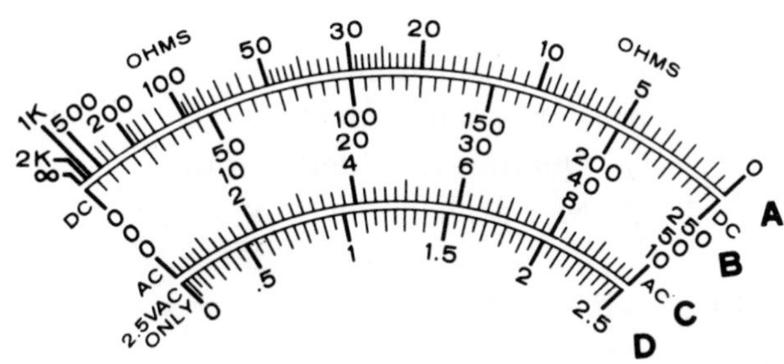

Figure U6-2
Figure for question 8.

9. What is the purpose of the battery in an ohmmeter?

A. Provide a reference voltage.
B. Supplement the current in the circuit being tested.
C. Supply current to the ohmmeter circuit.
D. Change meter ranges.

10. A simple DC voltmeter circuit consists of a 1 milliamp, 5000 ohm meter movement and a 5000 ohm multiplier resistor. What is the full-scale voltage for this meter?

A. 0.5 V.
B. 1.0 V.
C. 10 V.
D. 250 V.

11. What causes ammeter insertion loss?

A. A high current through the meter movement.
B. Too small a value of shunt resistance.
C. The resistance of the ammeter circuit.
D. No voltage dropped across the ammeter.

12. Which meter has a non-linear scale that reads from left to right?

A. Ohmmeter.
B. AC voltmeter.
C. DC voltmeter.
D. Milliammeter.

13. What part of the voltmeter scale should you use to get the most accurate reading?

    A. Full-scale deflection.
    B. Zero-scale deflection.
    C. Quarter-scale deflection.
    D. Mid-scale deflection.

14. What part of the ohmmeter scale should you use to get the most accurate reading?

    A. Full-scale deflection.
    B. Mid-scale deflection.
    C. Zero-scale deflection.
    D. Infinite-scale deflection.

15. What is the first step in making a resistance measurement with an analog ohmmeter?

    A. Connect the unknown resistor to the ohmmeter leads.
    B. Measure the voltage of the battery in the ohmmeter.
    C. Zero the ohmmeter.
    D. Measure the lead resistance.

16. To avoid damaging the meter movement of an ammeter or voltmeter, what procedure should you follow when making a measurement?

    A. Select the lowest range before connecting the meter, then increase the range until a satisfactory reading is obtained.
    B. Connect the meter first, then select the function and range.
    C. Select the highest range before connecting the meter, then decrease the range until a reading near full-scale is obtained.
    D. The sequence of function and range selection is not important.

17. Refer to the VOM meter scale shown in Figure U6-3. The selector switch is in the OHMS X100 position. What value of resistance is being measured?

A. 80 ohms.
B. 120 ohms.
C. 800 ohms.
D. 1200 ohms.

18. If the VOM selector is in the 25 mA DC position for the reading shown in Figure U6-3, what is the value measured?

A. 1.86 mA.
B. 7.3 mA.
C. 18 mA.
D. 180 mA.

19. If the 500 VAC range is selected, what is the value indicated on the meter shown in Figure U6-3?

A. 72 V.
B. 180 V.
C. 186 V.
D. 365 V.

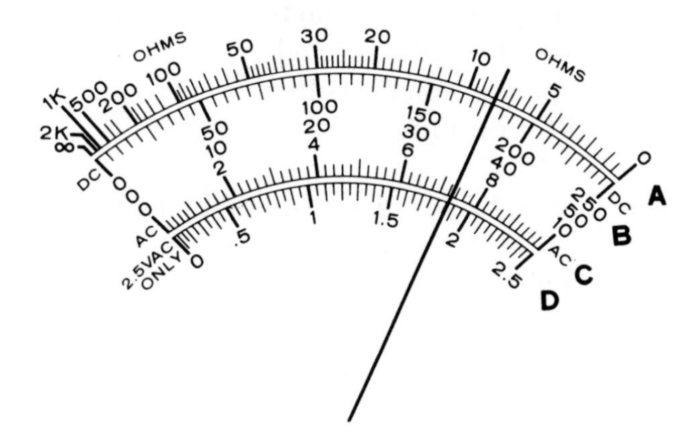

Figure U6-3
Figure for questions 17 through 19.

20. The accuracy specification for a VOM is ±3% of full-scale. The 250 VDC range is selected and the reading is 150. What is the range of possible values for the actual voltage?

A. 125.0 to 175.0 V.
B. 135.0 to 165.0 V.
C. 142.5 to 157.5 V.
D. 145.5 to 154.5 V.

21. What determines the maximum sensitivity of an analog ammeter?

A. The construction of the meter movement.
B. The value of the shunt resistor.
C. The ambient temperature.
D. The value of the multiplier resistor.

22. What values are used to define the sensitivity of an analog voltmeter?

A. Volts/ohm.
B. Ohms/volt.
C. Degrees-of-arc/volt.
D. Volts/ampere.

23. What can you say about the input resistance of a digital voltmeter?

A. It is constant for all ranges and typically equals 10 megohms.
B. It depends on the range selected.
C. It varies depending on the voltage measured.
D. It is typically very low.

24. What is the range of values a 3-1/2-digit digital meter can display?

A. 000.0 through 999.9.
B. 5000 through 9999.
C. 0000 through 1999.
D. 0.000 through 1.999.

25. When the range "200" is selected on a 3-1/2-digit digital meter, what are the range of values you can measure?

A. 000.0 through 200.0.
B. 000.0 through 299.9.
C. 100.0 through 199.9.
D. 000.0 through 199.9.

NAME ____________________

DATE ____________________

ANSWER SHEET FOR EXERCISE 1

Resistance

FIRST COLOR	SECOND COLOR	THIRD COLOR	FOURTH COLOR	FIFTH COLOR	CODED VALUE	TOL. %	MEASURED VALUE
orange	black	gold	gold	—			
red	violet	black	gold	—			
brown	black	brown	gold	—			
red	violet	brown	gold	—			
yellow	violet	brown	gold	—			
gray	red	brown	gold	—			
brown	black	red	gold	—			
brown	green	red	gold	—			
red	black	red	gold	—			
orange	gray	orange	brown	brown			
yellow	black	red	brown	brown			
green	blue	red	gold	—			
blue	black	yellow	brown	brown			
blue	gray	red	gold	—			
brown	black	orange	gold	—			
brown	red	orange	gold	—			
brown	green	orange	gold	—			
red	black	orange	gold	—			
red	violet	orange	gold	—			
orange	black	orange	gold	—			
yellow	black	red	red	brown			
yellow	green	orange	red	brown			
brown	orange	yellow	gold	—			

Figure E1-3

Resistor identification chart.

5. ________Ω

6. ________

7. ________Ω

____

____

8. ________Ω

____

____

10. 18-inch copper wire ________Ω

18-inch nichrome wire ________Ω

9-inch nichrome wire ________Ω

____

____

11. Light LDR ________Ω

Dark LDR ________Ω

____

____

12. ________Ω

NAME ____________________

DATE ____________________

ANSWER SHEET FOR EXERCISE 2

Ohm's Law

4. ________mA

5. ________V

6. ________

7. ________mA

8. ________V

____

____

11. ________V

____

____

____

14. ________mA

15. ________Ω

18. ________Ω

____

____

20. ________mA

21. ________mA

____

____

23. ________Ω

24. ________

25. ________Ω

28. ________

____

____

____

29. ________mA

____

____

30. ________W

31. ________Ω

32. ________mA

____

____

33. ________V

________Ω

34. ________Ω

____

____

NAME ____________________

DATE ____________________

ANSWER SHEET FOR EXERCISE 3

Series Circuits

5. ________V

6. ________V

____

8.

RESISTOR	OHMS	MEASURED CURRENT	CALCULATED VOLTS	MEASURED VOLTS
R1				
R2				
R3				

9. ________V

10. ________V

____

13. ____

____

14. ________V

____

____

15. ______________________________

____

17. ________Ω

18. ________V

19. ________mA

20. ________V

____

21. ________mA

____

22. ______________________________

____

26. ________mA

________Ω

27. ______________________________

____

28. ________mA

________mA

____

____

____

29. ________mA

____

____

____

____

NAME ____________________

DATE ____________________

ANSWER SHEET FOR EXERCISE 4

Parallel Circuits

3. ________mA

   ________V

4. ____

   ____

5. ________V

6. ________mA

   ________mA

7. ________mA

   __________mA

8. ________Ω

   ________Ω

9. ________Ω

   ________Ω

   ________Ω

10. ________Ω

12. ________

    ____

    ____

13. __________mA

__________mA

14. __________mA

__________Ω

__________Ω

____

15. __________Ω

16. __________mA

__________Ω

____

NAME ____________________

DATE ____________________

ANSWER SHEET FOR EXERCISE 5

Series-Parallel Circuits

3. ________mA

5. ____

____

6. ________mA

____

____

7. ____

____

________mA

9. ____

____

____

10. ________mA

________V

________mA

________V

11. ____

____

________mA

12. ________mA

________V

________mA

________V

14. ________mA

15. ________Ω

17. ________Ω

________mA

18. ________mA

____

19.

	CALCULATED VOLTAGE	ACTUAL VOLTAGE
R1		
R2		
R3		
R4		

NAME ______________________

DATE ______________________

ANSWER SHEET FOR EXERCISE 6

Magnetism, Solenoids, And Relays

1. __________
   ____
   ____

2. ____
   ____

3. ____
   ____

4. __________

12. ____
    ____

13. __________
    ____
    ____

20. ____
    ____
    ____

26. ________Ω

28. ________V

29. ________mA

30. ________V

31. ________mA

____

____

____

32. ________Ω

____

33. ________Ω

____

34. ________Ω

NAME ______________________

DATE ______________________

ANSWER SHEET FOR EXERCISE 7

DC Motors

4. ____

____

5. ____

____

6. ____

____

Why? ______________________________________

____

____

7. __________

____

8. __________

____

____

11. ________

____

____

____

12. ________Ω

____

____

____

13. ________

16. ________V

________mA

________V rms

________W

________W

NAME ________________

DATE ________________

ANSWER SHEET FOR EXERCISE 8

AC Characteristics

8. ________

____

9. ________

10. ________

11. ________

____

12. ____

____

13. ________

14. ________

15. ________

16. ________

19. ________

____

____

____

22. ________

23. ________

NAME ____________________

DATE ____________________

ANSWER SHEET FOR EXERCISE 9

Ohm's Law And AC

3. ________
   ____

4. ________
   ____

6. ________
   ____
   ________Ω

7. ________Ω
   ____

8. ________
   ____
   ____

9. ________
   ____
   ________Ω
   ____

10. ________
    ____
    ____
    ____

NAME ____________________

DATE ____________________

ANSWER SHEET FOR EXERCISE 10

DC Generators

3. ____
____

4. __________
____
____

5. __________
____
____

12. ____
____
____

13. ____
____

NAME ______________________

DATE ______________________

ANSWER SHEET FOR EXERCISE 11

AC-To-DC Conversion

3. ____

____

4. ____

____

____

6. ____

____

7. ____

____

8. ____

____

10. ____

____

Why? ____

____

11. ___________

____

____

12. ___________

____

____

NAME ____________________

DATE ____________________

ANSWER SHEET FOR EXERCISE 12

The d'Arsonval Meter Movement And The DC Ammeter

5. ________ mA

   ________ V

   ________ Ω

   ____

6. ________

8. R2 = ________ Ω

   R3 = ________ Ω

   R4 = ________ Ω

12.

BREADBOARD AMMETER CURRENT	MEASURED CURRENT	PERCENT ERROR
2 mA		
4 mA		
6 mA		
8 mA		
10 mA		
0.2 mA		
0.4 mA		
0.6 mA		
0.8 mA		
1 mA		

15. ________Ω

________Ω

________mA

16. ________mA

17. ________mA

19.

BREADBOARD AMMETER CURRENT	MEASURED CURRENT	PERCENT ERROR
20 mA		
40 mA		
60 mA		
80 mA		
100 mA		

22.

BREADBOARD AMMETER CURRENT	MEASURED CURRENT	PERCENT ERROR
0.2 mA		
0.4 mA		
0.6 mA		
0.8 mA		
1 mA		

NAME ________________

DATE ________________

ANSWER SHEET FOR EXERCISE 13

The Voltmeter

1. R1 = ________Ω

   R2 = ________Ω

   R3 = ________Ω

6.

BREADBOARD VOLTMETER VOLTAGE	MEASURED VOLTAGE	PERCENT ERROR
0.2 V		
0.4 V		
0.6 V		
0.8 V		
1 V		
2 V		
4 V		
6 V		
	7.5 V	—
8 V		
10 V		

11.

BREADBOARD VOLTMETER VOLTAGE	MEASURED VOLTAGE	PERCENT ERROR
6 V		
12 V		
18 V		
24 V		
30 V		

15. __________V

__________Ω

__________V

16. __________V

__________V

__________V

__________V

17. __________V

__________V

__________V

__________V

__________V

__________V

____

____

____

20.

BREADBOARD AC VOLTMETER VOLTAGE	MEASURED AC VOLTAGE
	1 V
	2 V
	3 V
	4 V
	5 V
	6 V
	7 V
	8 V
	9 V
	10 V

22. ____________V

____________V

____________V

NAME ____________________

DATE ____________________

ANSWER SHEET FOR EXERCISE 14

The Ohmmeter

1. ________Ω

5.

NOMINAL RESISTOR VALUE	BREADBOARD OHMMETER READING	MEASURED RESISTANCE VALUE
1500 Ω		
3830 Ω		
6800 Ω		
12 kΩ		
27 kΩ		
45.3 kΩ		

6. ________Ω

7.

NOMINAL RESISTOR VALUE	BREADBOARD OHMMETER READING	MEASURED RESISTANCE VALUE
100 Ω		
270 Ω		
470 Ω		
1000 Ω		
2000 Ω		
6040 Ω		